中国国家汉办赠送
Donated by Hanban, China

Chinese Lifestyle

CHINESE PHYSICAL EXERCISES AND HEALTH CARE

Wang Kaiwen
Qu Jianmei
Sun Lixia
Revision by Du Zhengming

CHINA
INTERCONTINENTAL
PRESS

图书在版编目（CIP）数据

中国人的健身养生：英文／王开文，曲建梅，孙丽霞编著.
—北京：五洲传播出版社，2011.1

ISBN 978-7-5085-1891-6

I.①中… II.①王… ②曲… ③孙… III.①健身运动－中国－英文
②养生（中医）－中国－英文 IV.① R161.1 ② R212

中国版本图书馆 CIP 数据核字（2010）第 175794 号

Chinese Lifestyle
Chief Editor: Du Zhengming
Planner: Deng Jinhui

CHINESE PHYSICAL EXERCISES AND HEALTH CARE

Authors: Wang Kaiwen, Qu Jianmei & Sun Lixia
Reviser: Du Zhengming
Executive Editor: Gao Lei
Art Director: Yang Jingfei
Publisher: China Intercontinental Press (31 Beisanhuanzhonglu, Haidian
District, Beijing 100088, China)
Tel: 86-10-82007837
Website: www.cicc.org.cn
Printer: Beijing Foreign Language Printing Co., Ltd.
Format: 710 × 1000mm 1/16
Edition: Jan. 2011, 1st edition, 1st print run
Price: RMB 86.00 (*yuan*)

Introduction to Chinese Lifestyle

China, a country of appealing mysteries.

The Chinese nation, a nation intermittently strong and weak, honorable and infamous, awake and asleep, with a history of five millennia at the shortest and probably longer, has experienced the highest stage of ancient civilizations in the most prosperous dynasties of the world, and made indelible contributions to the advance of human societies. As the world's biggest nation, the Chinese people account for approximately a quarter of the whole population on earth.

And as a standing member of the UN Security Council, it is exerting enormous influence on international affairs. Economically speaking, it is the world's largest consumer market and human resource reservoir, as well as the largest base of processing industries.

For the recent three decades, China's opening to the world has brought about unprecedented contact with the people of all other countries, resulting in great advancement of the Chinese society and drastic growth of its economy, which have drawn ever greater attention of the world.

Now again as in the past when China was in its prime, the world find it impossible to overlook China and its people.

However, for its many sufferings in pre-modern and modern history of social unrest and setbacks, natural disasters and social misfortunes, China has for a long time remained relatively backward, listed as a "developing country" of the world. And for the same reason, The Chinese people and their civilization have been neglected in the developed countries, and what is now known of China to quite many people in the West remains to be what it was 30 or 50 years ago.

In view of the above conditions, we hereby present to our readers this brand-new *Chinese Lifestyle* with the aim to help those interested in things Chinese learn about the people and their social life, and ultimately discover "the last hidden world" and the nation that is once more on the rise in the Oriental, so as to more effectively communicate with them in all walks of life.

Within this series are five books, respectively on the language, folk culture, rites and rituals, traditional food, and traditional physical exercises of the Chinese people. Drawing upon vast resources from libraries and internet materials, these books are all written with special perspectives of the writers themselves, and infused with their individual insight. What's more, the style of the language may also be interesting to the western English readers because the writers are all native Chinese themselves who teach English in higher institutions of education in China. This means that their English language may smack of some "Chinese flavor," somewhat different from that of the native English writers but nevertheless are pleasantly readable after minor revision by invited native English first readers.

Chinese Language by the undersigned chief-editor of this series begins by a general introduction of various "Chinese languages," languages of different Chinese ethnic groups as well as the majority Han people. The relation between Mandarin Chinese and Chinese dialects is also explained with fair clarity. Through reading the introduction, you will learn why Mandarin Chinese has become "the Common Language" (Putonghua) of the nation, how Chinese written characters evolved into the present form, and what differences exist between the classic and modern language, and between the formal written style and informal speech. In addition, the systems of Mandarin Chinese Pinyin and Tones are introduced in detail to serve as a threshold for exploring the contents of the book.

After the introduction are six chapters elaborating on the distinctive features of Mandarin Chinese, respectively in terms of its phonology, tones, morphology and syntax. In each chapter, typical and practically usable examples are provided along with annotation of the tones and translations, so as to help readers learn with ease.

Chinese Rites and Rituals is written by Feng Ge (冯鸽), an associate professor with the Northwest University, and translated by Huang Jieting (黄洁婷) and Jiang Yinji (蒋茵佶), English teachers of Suzhou Vocational University. It is an overall introduction of the Chinese ritual systems and the related social norms. The first part begins with an elaboration of the central Chinese concept *Li* (礼), which carries a wide range of connotations including not only rites and rituals but also what are generally concerned as good manners, appropriate behavior and acceptable ceremonies on various social occasions. The contents are divided into two parts, with the first part on traditional rites and rituals and the second on the modern practice. Actually all possible aspects appropriate to be considered under the general title of *Li* are touched on, from individual social conducts to state rules. With the understanding that *Li* is a matter of great importance in Chinese culture, we believe this book is of special value for learning about the Chinese society and the people's way of thinking and life.

From *Chinese Food Life Care*, authored by Yang Hua (杨婳) and Guo Wen (郭雯), lecturers of English at Soochow University of Science and Technology, readers are expected to learn about the traditional Chinese way of eating, and find their opinions as regards the choices of food in various situations. They will also familiarized themselves with a great variety of traditionally consumed Chinese food items and understand why some items are more popular than others in China, and why the Chinese people generally believe "food and medicine are of the same origin." It is our hope that the detailed accounts of the properties of different food items will serve as useful references for making decisions on what one should choose to eat according to his or her own physical conditions.

Chinese Physical Exercises and Health Care was written by Professor Wang Kaiwen (王开文), an expert in Chinese Kungfu and Taijiquan, and Qu Jianmei (曲建梅) and Sun Lixia (孙丽霞), Teachers of English at Yantai University. It begins with a brief account of the basic knowledge of Chinese Physical Exercises and Health Care, a short History of the Development of various ways of traditional physical exercises such as Taijiquan and Qigong, the Basic Theories concerning their efficacy and mechanism, and the methods generally adopted in practice. Then, in the following chapters are presented the concrete procedures of exercises, all well illustrated with clear pictures to aid the practitioner. In addition, traditionally practiced supporting like various ways of self-massage is also introduced at length. It is our belief that the explanations and illustrations will not only make the reading of the book an effortless experience but also help in practice.

Chinese Folk Customs, by Zhang Weihua (张伟华) and Fang Huawen (方华文), projects before the readers a changing and kaleidoscopic view of the Chinese social phenomena seen in different areas and ethnic communities, in both the ancient times and present. Although it is understandably difficult for the writers to account for how much or to what extent the old customs have lasted to date, we can well assume that quite a lot have, even though possibly in somewhat changed forms. At any rate, they should have some unelectable impact on the Chinese contemporary way of life. And with growing consciousness of the importance of protecting traditional culture, some wholesome folkways that had once fallen to the verge of extinction are now being recovered, while others are still often found in Chinese literary works even if they have fallen out of date. Thus, reading about them should be awarding, and as I hope could also be a pleasure.

The five books in this *Chinese Lifestyle* on the whole form a kind of knowledge pool for readers interested in the Chinese society, the people and their way of thinking and social behavior. And I believe they will be of very practical use for those who are presently working in China or considering a visit or some time of stay here. And for those who have the interest in Chinese literature, the contents should also be something worth reading.

In the end, I feel obliged to acknowledge the help of many who have given me very good suggestions as regards the contents of the books, including in the first place Professor Fang Huawen, my colleague at Soochow University and a proliferate writer. And of special help in making this series publishable is Mr. Deng Jinhui (邓锦辉) at China International Press, who has cooperated with me from the very beginning of the planning through to the end. Without his far-sighted vision of the possible readership and their expectations, all efforts may be just spent for nothing.

March 19, 2010
Du Zhengming (杜争鸣)
Professor of English
Soochow University
Suzhou, China

Contents

Chapter One

Brief Introduction to Chinese Physical Exercises and Health Care

1 Brief History of Development

Traditional Chinese physical exercises and health care are the crystallization of life care practice in the nation's thousands of years of life and productivity, especially with regard to its fight against disease. As a kind of the treasures of the Chinese culture, it plays a significant role in the nation's civilization and prosperity and has made great contributions to the development and progress of Chinese physical and medical sciences. The exercises include Wushu, Qigong and other forms of practice with Chinese characteristics.

Boasting a long history, traditional Chinese physical exercises and health care have been developing in a continuous course of improvement through practice, forming a unique methodology and theoretical system of its own. The theory, belonging to the domain of human physical sciences, originated from Traditional Chinese Medicine (TCM), but has also adopted key ideas of classical Chinese philosophy. In terms of development, its evolution has followed the sequence of *Dao-Yin-Shu* (Physical and Breathing Exercise 导引术), *Wu-Qin-Xi* (Five-

The Physical and Breathing Exercise Picture (Recovery), 202 BC-8 AD, unearthed in Changsha, Hunan Province, containing 44 charts of both men and women with brief instructions on ailment treatment and health care.

Animal Play 五禽戏), *Ba-Duan-Jin* (Eight-Section Health Exercise 八段锦), *Yi-Jin-Jing* (Changing Tendons Exercise 易筋经), and Taijiquan.

Dao-Yin-Shu, which dates back to the end of the primitive society, is an ancient way to keep fit and healthy. It is related to ancient Chinese witchcraft as well as the natural environement. It is said that *Xiao-Zhong-Wu* (消肿舞), invented by Yinkang to prevent and treat joint ailments during the period of the Five Legendary Rulers (2600-2070 BC), was the earliest health care physical exercise and a precedent of *Dao-Yin-Shu*. The word *Dao-Yin* first appeared in *Chuang Tzu* (book of the famous Taoist Chuang Tzu), in which breathing and the acts imitating the tree-climbing of bears and the flying of birds were related for achieving fitness and good health, and preventing aging. *Dao-Yin-Shu* was thus taken as a combination of breathing and body movements for the purpose of health care and the treatment of diseases. It was supplemented with self-massage after the Han Dynasty (206 BC-220 AD).

Dao-Yin-Shu took form in its early development in the Eastern Zhou Dynasty (770-256 BC). This special physical exercise based on breathing then became a particular inquiry named Qigong. The Han Dynasty was an important period for its development, for

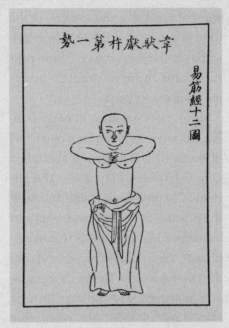

Yi-Jin-Jing Form I, in *Nei Gong Tu Shuo: Illustrated Explanation of Nei Gong* 1858.

The Physical and Breathing Exercise Picture unearthed from the Mawangdui Han Dynasty tombs at Changsha is the earliest and most complete on it so far. The picture contains 44 charts, each describing a separate movement in the exercise. These charts depict both men and women, old and young alike, some of whom are clothed, some barebacked, with some people standing and others sitting. The charts delineate general exercises and particular actions for specific ailments, breathing methods, imitation of animal movements, and exercises either with or without tools. Each act is separately presented, illustrating different ways of breathing and exercise of the time when it was made. There are some similarities between these postures and those of modern body-building exercises.

Since most postures in early *Dao-Yin-Shu* were imitating the movements of animals, the exercise was also called *Qin Xi* (Animal Play 禽戏). The ancient TCM physicians mainly followed the practice of body movements and massage while the Taoists would emphasize the control of breath and conduct the intrinsic *qi*. The exercise gradually matured during the Chinese Middle Ages (200-581 AD), when more movements were added to it and classified into different sets. Moreover, many works specializing in health care were written during this period. In the Sui and the Tang Dynasties (581-907 AD), preceding ways of health care and disease treatment were collected and compiled; concerned theories were also proposed, which marked a major breakthrough in its development. From the Song to the Qing Dynasty (907-1911 AD), such great innovations as *Yi-Jin-Jing* and Taijiquan were made and promoted further development of *Dao-Yin-Shu*.

Inspired by the different animal movements, the famous TCM physician Hua Tuo (141-208 AD) devised the so-called Five-Animal Play which mimicked the movements of five animals: the tiger, deer, bear, monkey and bird. The appearance of this exercise marked the new stage of the development of *Dao-Yin-Shu* and opened up broad prospects for the invention of other body-building and health-keeping exercises. The initial chart of this exercise has already been lost; the edition that has been handed down to this day was recorded by Tao Hongjing (456-536 AD) in his *Collection of Ways to Protect Health and Deter Aging*. Though large in variety, most of the popular protocols at present

Hua Tuo (141-208 AD), a well-known Chinese physician, devised Five-Animal Play mimicking the movements of five animals: tiger, deer, bear, monkey and bird to keep fit, cure diseases and deter aging.

were compiled by later practitioners in his name, some emphasizing internal exercise, others underlying techniques of combating.

Developing into the Song Dynasty (960-1279 AD), Chinese traditional health care exercises made their most remarkable achievement by inventing an exercise that is practiced while sitting. An example of it is seen in *Ba-Duan-Jin*, which consists of eight sections, including sitting postures and standing postures. The whole set of sitting postures includes dry bath (bathing hands, arms, head, eyes, nose, chest, legs, knees), beating the heavenly drum, revolving the eyes, tapping the teeth, resonant gargling, holding-rotating *yaoyan* acupoint (about 3.5 *cun* lateral to the lower border of the spinal process of the fourth lumbar vertebra), holding-rotating arch and rubbing abdomen. In contrast with standing postures, these movements are fine and delicate with moderate intensity. When it came to the Qing Dynasty (1644-1911 AD), *Shi'er-Duan-Jin* (The Twelve-section Health Exercise 十二段锦) and *Shiliu-Duan-Jin* (The Sixteen-section Health Exercise 十六段锦) were developed on the basis of sitting postures. They combined body movements with massage and breathing exercises and were widely practiced.

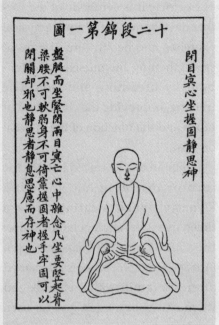

Shi'er-Duan-Jin Figure I, in *Nei Gong Tu Shuo: Illustrated Explanation of Nei Gong* 1858.

Another simple and practical exercise called *Xiao-Lao-Shu* also appeared in the Song Dynasty. Practicing principles such as "gradual and moderate practice in accordance to one's capability" and "perseverance" were proposed. At the end of the Ming Dynasty (1368-1644 AD), Yi-Jin-Jing was invented and later spread widely in the Qing Dynasty. In Chinese, *yi* means "change," *jin* means "tendons or sinews," while *jing* means "methods." It was clearly stated by the compiler that this exercise program was effective enough to improve one's physique. As a relatively intense form of exercise, it is symbolic of the further development of Chinese physical exercises and health care. It aims at strengthening the muscles and tendons by breathing and isometric training, improving the circulation of blood and the function of the internal organs.

Taijiquan can be traced back to the turn of the Ming and the Qing Dynasty. When nearing modern times, five styles or schools took shape: the *Chen*, *Yang*, *Wu (Jianquan)*, *Wu (Yuxiang)* and *Sun* schools are named after the families that established them. Although each has its own forms, postures, and movements, their essence remains the same. The practice, which connects the spiritual and the physical worlds, is characterized by graceful, slow, harmonious, and smooth movements of body and mind-intention.

While we are summarizing the formation and development of Chinese physical exercises and health care, we can find that the history of *Dao-Yin-Shu* is at the same time the history of Qigong. There are similarities as well as differences between them in both theory and practice. While both of them are the dynamic combination of breathing actions and body movements, the former stresses body movements and the latter focuses on the mind-intention.

Since the founding of the People's Republic of China in 1949, a mass movement of body-building and health preservation has been flourishing. It is in the 1950s that the word "Qigong" was first put forward. Many Qigong research institutes and Qigong sanitariums were established afterwards. Qigong has been recognized as a branch of human physical sciences to benefit all of mankind.

Records show that Chinese *Dao-Yin-Shu* had spread to Japan and North Korea by the 10th century. By the 18th century it had been introduced to Europe by French missionaries and exerted a vital influence on the establishment of one of the cornerstones of modern physical exercises—Swedish gymnastics, which was rare in the recent history of East-West cultural exchanges. Since the 1960s, the function of Qigong has gained attention from the scientific communities in Europe, America, Japan, and Russia. Comprehensive research has been made in this field. Qigong schools have been set up in Sweden; courses on it are now obligatory for American and Russian astronauts and have been taught in the geriatrics colleges of France; three international symposiums on Qigong have been held since 1973.

In China, Chinese Qigong Joint Performances in July, 1979 promoted the widespread practice of Qigong, which was continuously pushed to a climax with the establishment of The National Association of TCM on Qigong in September, 1981. In addition to the traditional exercises, such as *Wu-Qin-Xi*, *Ba-Duan-Jin*, *Yi-Jin-Jing* and Taijiquan, new exercises are also explored, strengthened and devised.

The introduction of traditional physical and healthcare exercises to schools has not only helped students to enhance intelligence, encourage ethics, protect health, and prevent diseases, which can benefit them for a life time, but has also promoted the popularity of physical exercises among the mass and made great contributions to people's health maintenance.

Since the 1980s, there has been a "Qigong Fever" all over the world. In this context, some people claim that they own "supernatural power" and are able to bring it into play. These claims are actually swindles in the name of "human body science." The aim was to disseminate superstition and con people out of their money. Some of them even turned into evil cults with certain political purposes and brought disaster to Chinese people. In fact, traditional *Dao-Yin-Shu* is simple and easy to learn, with no religious mystery. Hence, as long as we understand its basic principles and movements, we can avoid being deceived.

II Basic Concepts and Theories

The Concept of Holism

Being the fundamental concept and one of the features of TCM, the idea of Holism gives particular emphasis on the unity and wholeness of matters and their relations. TCM believes that the constituent parts of the human body are inseparable in structure, related with and conditioned by one another in physiology. Meanwhile, the human body is also conditioned by the natural environment in the way that the former dynamically adapts to the latter and maintains its normal functions. This recognition of the interrelated nature of the body's components and the balance between the body and nature are defined as the concept of Holism. It is the theoretical basis for Chinese traditional physical exercises and health care, applied throughout the process of TCM treatment, such as diagnosis, healing and recovering.

As a matter of fact, the concept of Holism that "Man corresponds with nature" is embodied in all the theories and practices of Chinese physical exercises and health care. Under the guidance of this concept, the ancient masters of health care paid close attention to the relationship between man and nature. The internal causes—joy, anger, anxiety, pensiveness, grief, fear, and fright are called "Seven Emotions," while the external causes—wind, cold, summer-heat, dampness, dryness, and fire are "Six Evils." Although the former type of causes is considered primary, the second is also stressed. The masters recommended the preservation of vital essence (*jing*), the replenishment of *qi*, and the cultivation of vitality (*shen*). The principles are "cultivating one's mind," "conforming to the change of the seasons," "eating a balanced and healthy diet," "observing a regular way of life," and "avoiding overworking." In terms of mind cultivation, they advocated keeping a happy mood and emotional balance, for the excessive changes in emotion may lead to disease. For correspondence with the law of nature, they advised that the change of the seasons and the climates should not be followed passively. Correct ways to maintain good health were suggested, such as active physical exercise, so as to improve one's physique to adjust to the climatic changes. With regard to diet, instead of preference for foods of certain tastes, the masters approved a balanced diet for providing all ingredients of nutrition needed by humans, regardless if the food is crude or delicate. As for daily life, they advocated adjusting one's living habits in accordance with the change of seasons. For example, in Spring, one should rest late and rise early to take a walk and enjoy the fresh air; in Summer, one should also go to bed late while getting up early, in spite of the burning sun; in Autumn, one should sleep early and rise early following the chicken's living rhythm; in Winter, one should repose early and get up at sunrise. As regards the avoidance of overwork, they were for working in a regular but mild way, rather than working in extreme intensity or to an overdue extent. Fatigue should be avoided. In their view, protracted watching disturbs the flow of blood; long sitting time impairs the muscles; longtime lying weakens *qi*; a long period of standing causes bone injuries; excessive walking does harm to tendons. Therefore, a habit of taking regular but moderate exercise should be formed and followed.

Yin Yang Theory

As a system of ancient Chinese philosophic thought, *Yin Yang* Theory is also a science to generalize and elucidate the laws of nature and those of the living system. It is believed that all things embody two aspects, *yin* and *yang*, the contradiction and harmony of which are the fundamental causes for the production, changes, and perishing of everything. The universe itself is the development of *yin* and *yang*, which oppose yet complete each other.

The basic contents of the *Yin Yang* Theory can be summed up in four words—opposition, interdependence, inter-penetration, and transformation. As a pair, *yin* and *yang* contradict each other. For example, while *yin* is regarded as the upper part of the body,

YinYang WuXing BaGua, in Yangzhou Museum of Chinese Medicine.

the interior, the *zang* organs, cold, and quietness, *yang* refers to the lower part of the body, the exterior, the *fu* organs, heat, and mobility. Interdependence means that *yin* and *yang* cannot exist in complete isolation from each another. Without "upper," there is no "lower;" without mobility, there is no quietness. Inter-penetration and transformation indicate changeability. For example, heat occurs when cold goes to extreme; brightness takes place when darkness gradually disappears. Thus, as is shown above, the basic contents of *Yin Yang* Theory are not isolated but correlated and interactive.

TCM holds that the dynamic balance of *yin* and *yang* in the movement and changes of the human organism maintains health and the normal function of body organs. In Chinese traditional physical exercises and health care, the harmony between *yin* and *yang* cultivates the flow of blood and *qi*, helps prevent disease, deter aging, and thus prolong life. Therefore, practitioners should remember that "there is *yin* inside *yang* and vice versa." So it is possible to restore a balance of *yin* and *yang* and to regain the state of harmony in the living system.

Five Elements Theory

The concept of Five Elements, literally meaning Five Movements, is developed from the concept of "Five Materials" referring to five indispensable and primordial substances in people's daily life and production activities.

The theory, which further extends the concept, claims that all things in the universe are generated from the movements of five elements—wood, fire, earth, metal and water, the relation among which is inter-promotion and inter-restriction. Inter-promotion means each element generates another and is therefore followed by one another. This productive cycle is in the following order: wood, fire, earth, metal, and water. Inter-restriction means each element conquers an element that follows it, but each is preceded by a conquering element. The controlling cycle, also known as the destructive cycle, repeats itself, with water controlling fire. The relation of the Five Elements shows the interrelation of all things and phenomena in nature, which should somehow maintain the state of balance in movements.

Theory of Zangfu Organs

Zangfu (viscera), a general term for internal organs, includes the five *zang* organs (the heart, liver, spleen, lungs, and kidneys), the six *fu* organs (the gallbladder, stomach, small intestine, large intestine, bladder, and triple energizer, including other extraordi-nary organs). The common physiological functions of the five *zang* organs are generating and storing vital essence, while the six *fu* organs receive, digest and transport food.

The heart, playing a leading role in all the viscera, provides motive power for blood circulation.

The liver is the primary organ for storing blood. It smoothes and regulates the flow of *qi* and blood by producing bile and purifying the blood.

The spleen rules transportation and transformation, which means it digests, absorbs, and distributes nutrient essences in the entire body. It can also command and control blood.

As the respiratory organs, lungs govern and exchange *qi*.

Being the prenatal base of life, the kidney, either one or a pair of organs in the lumbar region, stores essence of life, rules water, governs the bones, and produces bone marrow. An abundance of kidney essence leads to the sufficiency of kidney *qi*, which in turn contributes to good health and ensures good eyesight and hearing. In addition to these attributes, "the gate of life" and uterus are also inside the domain of the kidney function.

The main physiological function of the gallbladder is to store bile to aid the digestive process. To store vital essence is its other function.

The stomach governs intake, i.e., it receives and digests ingested foodstuffs. Playing an important role in life, it functions together with the spleen, and is called the "root of acquired constitution."

The small intestine receives what the stomach has not completely digested and further digests it. It also separates the "pure" (useful) from the "impure" (waste).

The large intestine receives the impure parts of the digested food from the small intestine and continues to absorb nutrients and water from these ingredients. At the end of this process, stools are formed and excreted.

The bladder is responsible for promoting *qi* flow, transforming *qi* into liquid, and storing and discharging urine.

The *triple energizer* is a collective term for the upper, middle, and lower energizer. The upper energizer is located above the diaphragm and includes the heart and the lungs; the middle energizer is the region above the belly button and below the diaphragm, including the spleen and the stomach; the lower energizer, which includes the liver, the kidneys, the large intestine, the small intestine, and the bladder, is located below the belly button. The triple energizer governs ingestion and is the channel for

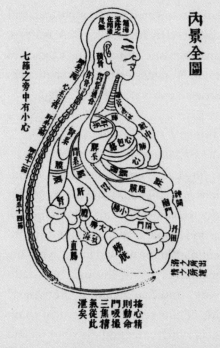

Picture of Internal Organs, in *An Introduction to Medicine* 1575 by Li Chan.

the transformation and metabolism of water, food, and fluid.

The functions of *zangfu* mainly depend on the *qi* of *zangfu*. The loss of one's genuine *qi* may result in the deficiency of *zangfu* organs. Therefore, the practicing process of Chinese traditional physical exercises and health care is also the process for cultivating the *qi* of *zangfu*. On the other hand, it is believed in TCM that seven emotions are closely related to the *qi* of *zangfu*. For example, "qi is driven upwards by rage, relieved by joy, inhibited by excessive anxiety, stagnated by pensiveness, consumed by excessive sorrow, lowered by excessive fear, and disturbed by fright." For these reasons, an optimistic attitude plus a peaceful mind is suggested to the practitioners so as to cultivate the *qi* of *zangfu*.

Theory of Meridians (Jing) and Collaterals (Luo)

Jing Luo, a general term for meridians and collaterals and the routes for the transportation and circulation of *qi* and blood, is an important constituent part in the human body, with *Jing* meaning "to pass through" or "pathway" and *Luo* meaning "network." Meridians refer to the vertical channels which carry and distribute *qi* and blood; collaterals branch off horizontally from the vertical channels and connects both *yin* and *yang* meridians; the smaller branches are called minute collaterals (*Sunluo*), running over the whole body in a crisscross fashion to smooth genuine *qi*. To sum up, *Jing Luo* is a unique system connecting the interior (the internal organs) and the exterior (body surface).

In the *Jing Luo* system, *Jing* consists of twelve regular meridians and eight extraordinary meridians, while *Luo* (collaterals) includes major collaterals (*Bieluo*), minute collaterals (*Sunluo*) and superficial collaterals (*Fuluo*). Besides, there are twelve muscle meridians (*Jingjin*) and twelve skin areas

Bronze Statue, 182.6cm in height with 664 accupoints and lines of meridians and collaterals labeled, built in the Qing Dynasty, now kept in the National Museum of China. Bronze statues were specially built for acupuncture teaching and testing.

(*Pibu*).

The twelve meridians are closely related to *zangfu* organs. It is composed of three *yin* meridians of hand (the Lung Meridian of Hand-Taiyin, the Pericardium Meridian of Hand-Jueyin, the Heart Meridian of Hand-

Shaoyin), three *yang* meridians of hand (the Large Intestine Meridian of Hand-Yangming, the Triple Energizer Meridian of Hand-Shanyang, the Small Intestine Meridian of Hand-Taiyang), three *yang* meridians of foot (the Stomach Meridian of Foot-Yangming, the Gallbladder Meridian of Foot-Shanyang, the Bladder Meridian of Foot-Taiyang), and three *yin* meridians of foot (the Spleen Meridian of Foot-Taiyin, the Liver Meridian of Foot-Jueyin, the Kidney Meridian of Foot-Shaoyin). Descending along the inner side of the arm, the three *yin* meridians of hand are interior and run from the chest to the hand; following the outer side of the arm, whereas three *yang* meridians of hand are exterior and run from the hand to the head. Distributed over the lateral and posterior aspects of the leg, three *yang* meridians of foot are exterior and run from the head to the foot. Ascending along the medial aspect of the leg, the three *yin* meridians of foot are interior and run from the foot to the stomach. The above-mentioned twelve meridians are known as the regular or principal channels. As the bond for the twelve regular meridians to flow *qi* and blood, the eight extraordinary meridians are *Du*, *Ren*, *Chong*, *Dai*, *Yangwei*, *Yinwei*, *Yangqiao*, and *Yinqiao* meridians. If the twelve meridians are

likened to the river, the extraordinary meridians are the swamp, balancing the genuine *qi* in the twelve meridians. Among them, *Ren* and *Du* meridians are the most important. *Ren*, a *yin* meridian running along the front midline, governs all the other *yin* meridians; *Du*, a *yang* meridian running along the back midline, governs all the other *yang* meridians. In Qigong practice, along with the connection of *Ren* and *Du* (the so-called minor celestial circle), all the other meridians and collaterals inside human body can be connected successively, thus forming up the so-called major celestial circle. (Fig 1-2-1~14)

Collaterals, which branch off from the twelve regular meridians, *Ren* and *Du* meridians, together with one spleen collateral, are called the fifteen major collaterals. The smaller and thinner ones are called minute and superficial collaterals.

The flow patterns of the twelve meridians are as follows: generally speaking, all *yin* meridians follow an upward order, while all *yang* meridians a downward order. Starting from the Hand-Taiyin Lung Meridian, it flows towards the Foot-Jueyin Liver Meridian. Then, it proceeds from the Lung Meridian of Hand-Taiyin and repeats the cycle. The meridian cycle is outlined below.

Fig 1-2-1

Fig 1-2-2

Fig 1-2-3

Fig 1-2-4

Fig 1-2-5

Fig 1-2-6

Fig 1-2-7

Fig 1-2-8

Fig 1-2-9

Fig 1-2-10

Fig 1-2-11

Fig 1-2-12

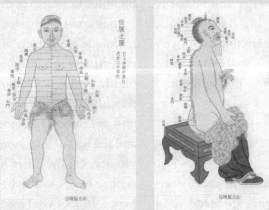

Fig 1-2-13

Fig 1-2-14

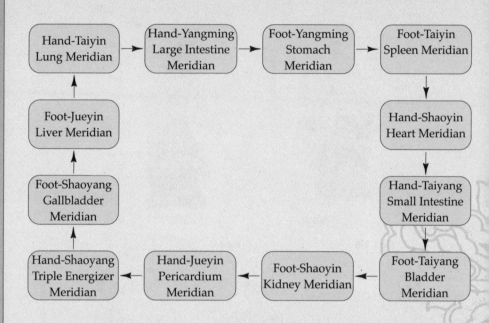

Important to TCM clinical application, the theory of meridians and collaterals is the basic theory of Chinese traditional physical exercises and health care. Through practice, *qi* is able to reach both the internal organs and the limbs and bones along the meridians and collaterals, providing sufficient energy to the tissue systems, quickening the metabolic process, and enhancing the physiological functions of the human body. Disease is therefore prevented and health improved.

Theory of Vital Essence, Qi, Vatality

Chinese traditional physical exercises and health care are made up of the inner exercise and outer exercise,

with the former aiming at strengthening vital essence, *qi* and vitality while the latter at the muscles, bones and skin. The ancient practitioners view the sun, moon, and stars as the three treasures of the sky, the water, fire, and wind the three treasures of the earth, and the vital essence, *qi*, and vitality the three treasures of the body, indispensable to the physical body.

Unique as they are, vital essence, *qi*, and vitality are inseparable. On one hand, vital essence houses vitality; thus, the accumulation of vital essence ensures the completeness of vitality and the loss of vital essence dislodges vitality. On the other hand, vital essence serves as the hothouse of *qi*; hence, lack of vital essence results in the non-existence of *qi* which leads to death. These three concepts existing in a complementary and interactive way are the crucial factors for maintaining the well-being of human life. Vital essence, the basis of life, is a congenital substance necessary for the origin of life. Consumed in the physiological activities, it is at the same time replenished and preserved to sustain life. Vitality governs the appearance, consciousness, or life activities. It is the reflection of the functions of the internal organs and hold sway above every aspect of the physical body. Its material base is created by the congenital essence, stored in *dantian* (elixir field) by the ingested nutrient essence and constantly replenished. *Qi* is viewed as the life force or the vital energy of the body. It is with the energy acquired from the preservation of *qi* that the functions of all body components are maintained. Without *qi*, vital essence cannot be regenerated, nor can vitality exist. Therefore, in order to keep the body physically strong with vigorous vitality, the cultivation of *qi* should be exercised in the first place. The major aims in health care are preserving vital essence, cultivating vitality, and replenishing *qi*, all aiming at preventing disease and deterring aging.

Stone Memorial for Traditional Chinese Healthcare in Pengzu Mountain, Sichuan Province.
Pengzu is regarded as the patron saint of chefs for curing the anorexia of an ancient emperor with his originality "pheasant soup." He also initiated *Dao-Yin Qigong* to guide *qi* and achieve longevity.

III Efficacy and Mechanism _____

The multi-efficacy and complicated mechanism of Chinese traditional physical exercises and health care have long been explored and expounded by *kungfu* practitioners and physicians of past ages. Four aspects concerned are meticulously selected and elaborated here.

Efficacy and Mechanism of Preventing Disease and Improving Health

1. Supporting vital qi and expelling pathogenic evils

TCM holds that the pathogenic factors are not the only factors resulting in disease, for the human body's resistance to various pathogens and health maintenance also count. Thus, to strengthen vital *qi* against diseases is one of the major aims of traditional physical exercises and health care. In the view of TCM, *qi* governs blood and blood depends on *qi* for its movement. When the flow of *qi* and blood becomes sluggish, disease occurs; but it can be cured automatically with the smooth circulation and transportation of *qi* and blood. Here *qi* has two kinds of existence: the first is the nutrient essence that forms the basis of human

body and maintains its life activities, for instance, the food essence and the fresh air; and the other is the physiological function of *zangfu* organs, hence we say as *qi* of *zangfu* and *qi* of *Jing Luo*. Correlated as they are, the former kind is the physical basis of the latter, the latter being the functional manifestation of the former. *Qi*, reaching the internal organs as well as the limbs and joints along the meridians and collaterals, is the fundamental force warming and nourishing muscles and *zangfu* organs, lubricating and moistening tendons, bones, skin and hair. With its ascending, descending, in-going and out-going movements, it tightens striae and guards against external evils. In light of the above argument, exercises are advocated to strengthen vital *qi* and remove various evils for keeping normal and regulated blood circulation, *zangfu* functions and metabolic activities, all for the purpose of improving health conditions.

2. Regulating psychoactivities and improving body functions

Through the practice of "relaxation" and "stillness," traditional physical and health care exercises regulate people's psychoactivities, upgrade body adjustment functions and improve antiviral ability. The principle "tranquility and nihility," i.e. wiping out distracting thoughts and focusing on relaxation, can ease the muscles and reduce the impact on the cerebral cortex so that "the state of relaxation response" can be achieved and the physiological function improved. For instance, according to the epidemiological study of hypertension, tension can affect some physiological indicators, and environmental pressure forces the human body to constantly regulate its activity, resulting in "emergency response" which leads to the increase of skeletal muscle bloodstream, the rise of blood pressure, the acceleration of heart rate and respiratory frequency. Instead, "relaxation response" weakens the activity of the nervous system, reduces the lactic acid content in arterial blood, decreases the metabolic rate, lessens the activity of the plasma dopamine, the ß-hydroxy acid and rennin, hence quickening the recovery of normal conditions. Furthermore, traditional physical and health care exercises enable people to feel at ease, eliminate negative emotions and morbid mentality, and thus effectively strengthen the central nervous system, respiratory system, digestive system and cardiovascular function.

3. Balancing *Yin* and *Yang*

The *Yin Yang* disharmony, one of the causes of disease in TCM, can be put right with the *dual modulation effect* by

People practicing Taiji on the square, Beijing, 1982.

containing the strong while supporting the weak. As found in experiments and clinical observation, when the practitioners attain stillness, the activity of his or her sympathetic nervous system declines, metabolic activities slow down, the state of high reaction is controlled and the hyperfunction is kept in check, all of which manifest the effect of Qigong exercise: restricting the excessive *yang* and restoring *yin*. On the contrary, after Qigong exercises, those with kidney *yang* deficiency will find that the content of ketonuria steroids in their body recovers to the normal level, the triphosadenine and cyclic amp content in blood plasma increases, and the immune function of white blood cells intensifies. All of this is the result of *yang* replenishment. Consequently, these practitioners will feel warmth in their limbs. Such effects can be seen at different levels and reflect the mechanism of traditional physical exercises of curing illnesses and protecting health.

4. Opening up channels of meridians and collaterals

According to TCM, soreness occurs when channels are blocked, and so blockages in meridians and collaterals are another cause of disease. As observed, those having meridian blockages which disturb the flow of *qi* and blood may suffer from body temperature inequality ranging from the extremely high to the extremely low. However, with the progress of exercise, the flow of *qi* and blood tends to get regulated. Due to the redistribution of blood, the peripheral vessels open, microcirculation improves, the blood flow volume in tissues increases and regional temperatures rise. Consequently, the difference of body temperature tends to be remarkably reduced and restore to balance. The thermal imager shows that when a person is practicing, wherever *qi* goes, brightness overwhelms while darkness succumbs and the bright spot moves with the mind-intention. The temperature rises by 2-4 or so and the regional blood flow volume increases by as much as 30%. Meanwhile, the activity of dopamine and ß-hydroxylase in blood plasma decreases while the eosinophil, erythrocyte and hemoglobin increases, immune response increases, and the secreted volume of plasma cortisone is halved. Hence, as is shown above, illness can be prevented or cured by dredging up channels of meridians and collaterals, and regulating *qi* and blood.

5. Deterring aging and prolonging life

Central neurotransmitter and endocrine gland activity tend to change during physical exercise. Therefore, as is measured, the practitioners will feel at ease and calm after practice, for it results in a decrease of the activity of dopamine, a central neurotransmitter, and an increase in the consistency of the prolactin in blood plasma. Furthermore, the decrease of the secreted volume of plasma cortine deters aging and enhances the immune system, thus preventing illnesses and prolonging life.

Efficacy and the Mechanism of Developing Body Potentials

Traditional physical and health-keeping exercises can improve the coordination of the human nervous system and protect the cerebral cortex by suppressing overdue activity, thus bringing human potential into full play and helping self-control. Physiological experiments have demonstrated that a large number of electroencephalograms recorded of men when

Wushu fan Tong Zhong-yi is practicing Wushu with his families on the park grass in Shanghai, 1957.

they are awake display high-frequency and low-amplitude waves with poor synchronization. However, the electroencephalograms made by Qigong masters are low in frequency but three times higher than normal people in amplitude, with very good synchronization. All these changes are most notable in the frontal and parietal lobes, which serve to direct the consciousness in the central nervous system. This proves that Qigong exercise is able to make the activities of cerebral cortex cells more orderly, and can thus improve the efficiency of brain function. It is also found through tests that the cerebral cortex is in a special process of being initiatively intra-suppressive when doing Qigong exercise. Relying on the protection of such a favorably suppressive process, the inordinate function of cerebral cortex cells caused by over-excitement can be restored to normal, the obstinate pathologic excitation foci can be transferred into suppressive state, and most of the nervous centralis can be renovated positively. All these changes are beneficial for improving the coordination of the nervous centralis between excitement and suppression and better directing the functional activities of all organs.

Research indicates that the potential of the human body is great but not fully brought into function. The number of human brain cells is about 14 billion or so, among which only several billions are usually tapped, and so there is still 80 to 90 percent to be done. Similarly, only part of other human organs, like blood capillary and alveolus, is used. After Qigong exercise, there are obvious changes in brain waves, an increase in lung capacity and enlargement in vascular volume. This shows that the human body's potential can be further tapped through Qigong. By keeping on it, we can change the modes of receiving, processing and storing information in brains and fully utilize the otherwise inactive cells, thus resulting in the improvement of human intelligence,

sensing capability and function of controlling one's own actions. This makes human vitality more exuberant and human beings more intelligent, living longer and healthier lives.

Efficacy and the Mechanism of Enhancing Body Function

Qigong exercise, by showing its preliminary effectiveness in improving people's competitive ability, treating their injuries, eliminating their fatigue and adjusting their state, has become a new trend in physical scientific research.

Treatment of sports injuries is generally about acupoint-pointing and self-practice Qigong, supplemented with medication, acupuncture and massage. Its mechanism is to mobilize and motivate the self-adjustment of the human body's physiological function, aiming at strengthening the vital *qi*, toning the root, nursing *yin* and *yang*, and clearing the channels in order to help with rehabilitation.

Qigong is a positive way to eliminate exercise-induced fatigue. On the one hand, Qigong exercise can accelerate the blood circulation and increase the expansion and contraction of lung cells, which leads to adequate supply of oxygen and energy, the elimination of accumulating lactic acid and the decrease of muscle soreness.

The Wushu master is teaching Five-Animal Play in Baohe Park, Hefei, Anhui Province, 1959.

addition, Qigong exercise, which can adjust the central nervous system, relax the muscles, hence reducing energy consumption and increasing energy storage to mobilize body potential, is an effective way to positive recovery.

Nowadays, Qigong or similar methods are adopted home and abroad as an approach to adjust athletes' competitive state and improve their scores. The results are often gratifying. It is

This function makes it beneficial for eliminating fatigue. On the other hand, Qigong exercise can improve the function of internal organs, whet the appetite, and accelerate the excretion of metabolites, thus promoting the restoration of the body. In found in preliminary attempts that Qigong exercise can indeed strengthen the self-control of central nervous system, overcome physical inertia, increase competition desire and responsive actions, all contributing to the enhancement of the athletic ability.

IV Fundamentals and Methods of Traditional Exercises and Health Care

1. Fundamentals

For the chronically ill as well as the physically weak middle-aged and elderly people, it is necessary to formulate a set of practical methods to engage them intentionally in traditional physical exercises for achieving self-regulation through the comprehensive exercise of the mind, *qi* and form, and for the regulation of higher nervous activities. In this respect, the following basic principles should be honored.

(1) Differentiation of treatment

Abundant in methods and specific forms, traditional physical and health care exercises vary in form depending on the differences between people, their illnesses, as well as location and time.

In TCM, illnesses can be ascribed either to *yin* or to *yang*. Since the occurrence and development of an illness results from the *Yin Yang* imbalance of the interior and the exterior, the therapy principle is to discharge the excess and nourish the deficiency so as to restore the normal harmonious state between *yin* and *yang*. Therefore, TCM treatment focuses on clearing the channels and collaterals supplementing with the emission of the pathogen to activate the circulation of *qi* and blood, remove the pernicious evils, and thus cure illnesses and restore health.

As a supporting therapy, traditional physical and health care exercises should be practiced with a scientific attitude to prevent any detrimental physiological reaction.

(2) Practicing with perseverance

In general, physical exercises should be practiced twice or at least once every day, repeating the whole set movements several times in each practice. An interruption will make previous efforts go to waste. The cyclical manner is also stressed, with particular attention given to continuation during the hottest and coldest days. Only with long-term practice can the exercise skills be consolidated and improved, with the spirit, virtue, self-restraint, and ethical morality cultivated and tempered. Morning exercise, though less effective sometimes, proves fruitful in every season. Practice has proven that the overwhelming majority of the practitioners exercising in the early morning make great achievements.

2. Exercise therapy

Physical and health care exercises, a supporting therapy, should be chosen in accordance with the causes of disease, the pathogenesis, and the role of Qigong, under the principle of *syndrome differentiation treatment*, so as to achieve the desired effect. If supplemented with medication in the course of practice, the efficacy will be better. The exercises can be applied to fight against the following diseases.

(1) Digestive diseases

The cerebral cortex regulates the reaction of the human body to the internal and external environment. Such factors as adverse mental stimulation, excessive nervous tension, anxiety, depression, or lack of proper rest and adjustment due to long-time mental work, all may cause brain dysfunction, pathological excitation foci and regulation failure of the subcortical central and autonomic nervous system in the secretion, activity, digestion and nutrition of the stomach, which in turn results in ulcers.

Inner-training Exercise, the top preference for people with the above symptoms, can relax the tension of the cerebral cortex while concentrating the mind in *dantian*. Through repeated practice, favorable excitation foci will be formed in the cerebral cortex and gradually eliminate the pathological excitement foci, thus through the rule of preponderance in *negative induction effect* helping the cerebral cortex resume its function in regulating internal organs, in particular the secretion, movements, digestion and nutrition of the stomach, to achieve a cure for the ulcer.

(2) Hypertension

Among the factors that trigger hypertension, some are related to mental stress. Hypertension pursues the following pathogenic mechanism: arteriole and precapillary sphincter spasms cause an increased amount of resistance in blood circulation, which gives rise to high blood pressure. Re-laxation-tranquility Qigong, requiring relaxation from the cerebral cortex to the body muscles, is the best choice for hypertension patients. In practice, with the help of mind-intention and breathing, practitioners will gradually feel relaxed from head to heel. Therefore, repeated practice is very effective in reducing the strain of the cerebral cortex and the tension of peripheral arterioles and the precapillary sphincter, with the effect of lowering blood pressure. In addition to Relaxation-tranquility Qigong, Taijiquan, Taiji Swordplay and Slow-walking Exercise are also beneficial to patients.

(3) Coronary heart disease

Coronary heart disease (CHD) results from myocardial hypoxia caused by atherosclerosis of the heart. Its pathogenic mechanism is associated with the metabolic disorder of the body lipids, hemodynamic changes and the changes of the artery wall, which are affected by the neuroendocrine dyscrasia. Since nervous overstrain and excessive mental work are the leading causes for neuroendocrine dyscrasia, CHD are particularly prevalent among the middle-aged and elderly workers in mentally stressful occupations. Therefore, Qigong, combining moving exercise with static exercise is most suitable for patients with CHD, owing to its function to relax the spirit and brain and its capacity to offer adaptive training to the heart. Standing Exercise, Slow-walking Exercise, Taijiquan and Taiji Swordplay are also among the options for treatment.

(4) Chronic bronchitis, emphysema and other diseases

These types of diseases are mainly induced by inflammation and the resulting bronchial obstruction, which in turn cause alveolar expansion, breathing difficulty, and at last, body hypoxia. The patients should choose such Qigong exercises as Six-word Exercise, Taijiquan, etc., to improve the lung ventilation function and activate breathing metabolism. While practicing, one should regulate breathing upon stillness, particularly abdominal breathing, so as to enhance the exhaling function of the lung and to relieve the symptoms of emphysema.

(5) Neurasthenia

Neurasthenia is generally attributed to overwork, long-term mental stress or ambivalent mental state. Most neurasthenia patients are easily excitable and cannot endure stimulation. When the influence of the excitatory process of the cerebral cortex is greater than that of the suppressive process, disorder in the transformative process will result. Therefore, static exercises reinforcing the inhibiting process of the cerebral cortex are their best choice, for instance, Sit-still Exercise, Standing Exercise, Relaxation-tranquility Qigong, etc.

(6) Cancer

Cancer, generally considered as one of the least curable diseases, makes patients excessively worried and depressed. In recent years, Qigong is used as a supporting therapy in the treatment of liver cancer, stomach cancer, intestinal cancer and lung cancer, and is found to be greatly effective in resisting the continuous invasion of the cancer cells and thus prolonging patients' life.

Cancer patients are advised to practice Qigong and Taijiquan out in fresh air. Before practice, psychological therapy is recommended to help patients build up confidence, lift the psychological burden, exert subjective initiative and actively combine medication with physical exercise. Static and moving exercises should be combined in the course of practice. The former, such as mind-concentration method can enhance the regulatory function of the cerebral cortex, thus contributing to the improvement of the function and anticancer ability of body systems and *zang* organs; the latter plays an important role in enhancing physique, strengthening vital *qi* and building up fitness.

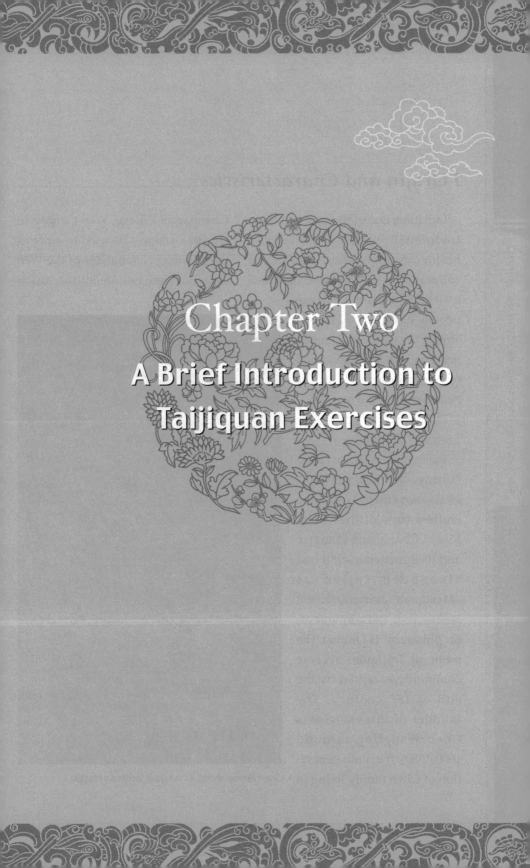

Chapter Two
A Brief Introduction to Taijiquan Exercises

1 Origin and Characteristics _____

Taijiquan, one of the major Chinese traditional physical exercises and health care approaches, is a national cultural legacy created and inherited by the common Chinese people. It has spread widely among the public and gained great popularity as a method to cure diseases, improve health and defend oneself.

Origin of Taijiquan

Taijiquan used to be called "Changquan" in its early time as its movement is like the endless flow of the "Long River" Changjiang (Yangtze and its upper course). It had also been called as "Mianquan" as its movement is slow, soft and continuous, or "Shisanshi" (13 forms). The name of Taijiquan became commonly accepted by the end of 18th century. The founder of this exercise is Chen Wangting (around 1600-1680), the ninth generation of Chen family living in Chenjiagou Village, Wen County in Henan Province. He used to serve as the garrison commander of the Wen County before retiring into seclusion

Chen Zhong-sheng, Chan Style Taijiquan Master

Yang Cheng-fu, Yang Style Taijiquan Master

Sun Lu-tang, Sun Style Taijiquan Master

in his later years. He compiled a new set of movements by integrating military and folk exercises and absorbing elements of Dao-Yin-Shu and Tu-Na-Shu, *Yin Yang* and *Jing Luo*. There are five sets of movements of his creation in *Chen Style Taijiquan and Weapons* edited by Chen's descendents, known as "Old Frame of Chen Style Taijiquan."

Many other styles or schools have been derived in the course of Taijiquan's development, including Yang's, Chen's New Form, Wu's (Jianquan), Woo's (Yuxiang) and Sun's etc. After the founding of PRC, Taijiquan forms have been recomposed into various simplified forms, such as the 24-form, 48-form, simplified Chen and Wu style Taijiquan. All the styles are similar in basic characteristics and technique structures, requiring peaceful and focused mind, natural breathing, soft and slow movements, smooth, complete, coordinative and continuous action, light and calm stances with a clear distinction between the empty and the solid. Besides Taijiquan sets of movements, pushing hands in free sparring and exercises of broad sword, sword and long staff are also included. As an effective way to keep fit and preserve health, it has already been popular both at home and abroad.

II Schools and Features

1. Chen style

Founded by Chen Wangting with five sets of movements in total, it nevertheless has only the first two sets of movements passed down and kept intact now, i.e. the thirteen forms and *Paochui*. Characterized by loose and low postures, spiral and winding moves. It emphasizes the smooth shift between loose, gentle and hard movements. There are also movements like *Fajin* (exerting strength or releasing power), jumping and stamping foot.

The above sets of movements are called "Old Frame of Chen Style Taijiquan" after reconstruction by Chen's descendents with some additional moves.

Chen Changxing (1771-1853), the 14th generation of Chen family, removed the forceful and jumping movements in the old frame and made it gentle and balanced, suitable for the feeble or aged to practice. Then Chen Qingping, the 15th generation, created another small and intensive frame advancing from simple movements to

A family of Taijiquan tradition, Chenjiagou, Wenxian County, Henan Province, 2002

Chen Shao-long (U.S.) and Chen Shao-bao (U.K.) are practicing Taiji Push hand in Chenjiagou, Wenxian County, Henan Province.

more complicated moves. The set of movements in the old frame gradually went out of practice after the new frame appeared.

2. Yang style

Founded by Yang Luchan (1799-1872) from Yongnian County in Hebei Province, who used to be called "Yang Wudi"(Invincible Yang) as he defeated plenty of *Wushu* boxers after eighteen years of training under Chen Changxing in Chenjiagou Village, the hometown of Chen family. Yang later was hired by the Chinese Qing royal family to teach Taijiquan all his lifetime, when he reformed the Chen style into a simpler Yang style. He removed the vigorous and abrupt movements, like jumps and leaps, and made it easy to practice. Yang Luchan passed his art to his sons Yang Banhou (1837-1892) and Yang Jianhou (1839-1917) and then to his grandson Yang Chengfu (1883-1936). After all their modification, it became the modern popular Yang style Taijiquan characterized by easy and soft frames, slow and steady movements and gentle and elegant gestures. Yang Chengfu who authored *Application of Taijiquan* and *Collection of the Application of Taijiquan* is one of the great masters of Yang style Taijiquan.

3. Wu (Jianquan) Style

Founded by Wu Jianquan (1870-1942) of Manchu ancestry. Wu's father Wu Quanyou used to be a disciple of Yang Luchan and Yang Banhou before teaching his son Jianquan. Later Jianquan abandoned his Manchu citizenship and changed his family name to Wu of the Han people. Evolved from Yang style Taijiquan, Wu style is famous for its softness and characterized by small and subtle movements.

4.Woo (Yuxiang) style

This style of Taijiquan was founded by Woo Yuxiang (1812-1880) from Yongnian County in Hebei Province who first learned big frame movements from Yang Luchan and then from Chen Qingping. It has a set of movements different from the style of Chen's small frame. However, it was finally formed after the modification of Li Yishe and Hao Weizhen, hence also known as "Hao style Taijiquan." The frame features light movements, swift steps, compact and continuous movements with obvious opening and closing forms.

5. Sun style

Founded by Sun Lutang from Ding County in Hebei Province. He was originally a disciple of Guo Yunshen, a famous master of Xingyiquan (literally "form-image boxing"), and then learned Baguazhang under Master Cheng Yanhua and Woo style Taijiquan under Master Hao Weizhen. Based on his early experience, Sun drew on all the strong points of other styles and created Sun style Taijiquan characterized by high postures, flexible steps and light-footed changes.

The above is the existing five major schools of Taijiquan. Besides, some new sets of movements were compiled after the founding of PRC.

6. The New style

24-form Taijiquan, the representative of the new style Taijiquan sets of movements compiled after the founding of PRC, was created and compiled by National Physical Culture and Sports Committee in 1956 and published by People's Sports Press in 1979. The set of movements were structured with the existing popular Taijiquan forms under the principle of practicing from simpler to more complicated and from easier to more advanced movements. It was a revolution in the history of Taijiquan exercise as it has changed the previous order which went from the more advanced to the easier, and removed some repeated moves, making it easier to learn and practice.

III Basic Requirements

All schools of Taijiquan have different characteristics and techniques, but they share similar and common requirements, which could be summarized as follows:

1. Be at ease, calm, and natural

This requirement, as a principle, is to be realized in the state of mind, breathing and forms. To be at ease and to be calm call to relax the body and curb the wandering mind, so as to focus one's attention on directing movements and exerting strength. To be natural means the manner and gestures should be naturally coordinating with natural breathing and movements.

2. Correct gestures

Head and neck

The head needs to be upright without exerting strength. Otherwise, it would not only affect the elegance of

Old people practicing Taijiquan in Lanzhou, Gansu Province, 1996.

the gestures but also the coordination and relaxation of the movements, resulting in distraction. Keeping the neck relaxed could help the head turn around easily in accordance with the fist movements. The facial expression should be natural and fresh with the eyes moving with the movement of one's hands or looking forward, the jaw slightly drawn back, the mouth closed and the tongue touching the palate. Breathe naturally and concentrate on the movements. Don't have a panning head, closed eyes or absent mind.

Torso

Keep it relaxed naturally. Do not protrude chest or draw it back too much. Keep waist relaxed, spinal column upright, and buttocks slightly pulled in. In a word, keep the body in a normal way.

Limbs

Movements of upper limbs require that both shoulders and elbow joints be relaxed and hung down, arms flexible and not rigid when stretched out or over-curved when bent; hands relaxed, calm, at ease and natural when formed into fists, stretched and overturned; palms and fists changing elastically, with the attention guided by hands.

Movements of lower limbs require a state of natural relaxation with re-laxed hips, bent knees, flexible ankles and a steady center of gravity. Steps should be ready to change between the empty and solid stance in forward or backward move. The movements should be firm and steady and coordinate with natural breathing.

3. Combination of the inner and the outer, completeness and unification

Taijiquan draws on the strong points of Wushu and Qigong with emphasis on the coordination of mind, breathing and movements and requires the unification of hands, eyes, bodywork, steps, spirit, *qi*, strength and practice. When the practitioner has advanced to a considerable level, he should incorporate the exercises of strength, mind-intension and breathing so as to complete the art.

The "force-strength" of Taijiquan means the natural power that keeps gestures correct. Its utilization should not be clumsy and rigid, but be coordinated in force and softness, with easy, flexible and calm movements. Though natural breathing is recommended at the beginning phase, the coordination between breathing and strength exertion should be consciously practiced after achieving the proficiency in the movements. Inhale with expanding thorax and lifting shoulders when saving strength and vice versa. Concentration is needed to guide movements. For instance, when practicing the opening form under the guidance of mind-intension, arms should be raised gently forward to shoulder height and then relax the waist, bend the knees and squat down, hands pressing down with the downward movement of elbows. Meanwhile, coordinate the above movements with breath—inhale when arms are raised and exhale when hands are pressing down so as to center mind on *dantian*.

Taijiquan movements would be practiced like the endless silk produced by the silkworm or the continuous water flow of the Long River Changjiang after the mastery of the whole routines. The changes in directions, empty and solid movements, and the coordination of the entire body would be like the rolling ball in a plate, shifting freely and flexibly. The upper part corresponds with the lower part with consistent vigor; the mind-intension changes with body movement, coordinating with breathing, all for complete "force-strength," and incorporation of the inner and the outer forces.

IV Points for Attention in Taijiquan Exercise

Beginners should practice according to the rules and basic requirements. Perseverant and correct practice will certainly bring about good results.

Three stages to beginners

Stage 1. Laying the foundation. Beginners should first learn the three basic skills: footwork, hand techniques and bodywork, the exercise of which will contribute to the mastery of basic requirements and lay a foundation for the set of movements learning.

Stage 2. Becoming familiar with set movements. Learn the set of movements one by one in order and then combine them together. Beginners are recommended to learn each analytical move within a single movement and then link them up. Having learned all the movements, they should gradually accomplish the whole routines by correcting gestures and familiarize themselves with the movements.

Stage 3. Practicing the exertion of strength. Gradually master the way to coordinate mind-intension, breathing and movements and to use mind to guide *qi* and exert strength so as to improve the technique and effects of the exercise.

Taijiquan players from 15 countries and regions led by Chinese American, Taijiquan master Dong Zeng-chen are practicing to celebrate the 108th brithday of Taijiquan Master Dong Ying-jie in Xingtai, Hebei province on Nov. 3, 2006.

Instructions to beginners

1. Gestures should be standard. Wrong gestures, affecting negatively both the appearance and the effect, will be hard to set right later if not corrected in time. Therefore, beginners should be strict with themselves and keep each movement standard.

2. Proper progress should be pursued. Learners should not expect a rapid progress or an immediate effect. Good results come only after steady and gradual improvements. The posture could be high at the beginning stage and lowered down gradually with the mastery of movements and the enhancement of health.

3. The amount of exercise should be appropriate. It will be proper if practitioners feel comfortable and relaxed, have good appetite and sleep well. Over-exercise will make them tired, dizzy or feel sick. Beginners should practice in accordance with their capabilities. They will have painful legs or knees if they place most of the weight on their extremities, which can be avoided if they raise the gravity center and reduce the bending level of knees. Keep on practicing and the uncomfortable feeling will gradually disappear.

4. To persevere. Taijiquan will not be restricted by place, equipment or time. As long as you keep practicing with determination, favorable effects will be achieved such as improving skill, building up health and preventing diseases.

Common knowledge for Taijiquan exercise

1. It's better to find a location with fresh air and beautiful surroundings, avoiding those dirty-aired or humid locations. Do not exercise in the burning sun, or in a draught or a fog.

2. It's not proper to exercise Taijiquan when you are restless, tired, too hungry or full, or having a fit of chronic disease, getting a cold or fever.

3. Go to the bathroom before exercise and wear loose-fitting and comfortable closes. Do some warming up exercise, like walking or some basic movements.

4. Keep calm and focused, and breathe through your nose. After exercise, it's proper to take a break, but not to have meal or drink large amount of water.

5. Beginners easily tire; therefore, they should restrict their exercise to an appropriate amount. The seniors and feeble practitioners could select single movements or separate the set of movements apart. It's not necessary for them to finish the whole set of movements once.

6. Practitioners with chronic diseases are advised to go through physi-

cal check-ups on a regular basis and do not quit from medical treatment completely. Keep sufficient sleep, regulate daily life and do the exercise in time and in optimistic attitude.

Taijiquan can keep people healthy, joyful and energetic. After reaching a certain degree, the practitioners will be so addicted to it as to be unwilling to stop practicing. Such delight and artistic conception have unique value in relieving fatigue, calming down nerves and increasing efficiency of work.

Chapter Three
A Brief Introduction to Qigong Exercises

1 Connotation of Qigong

With a variety of nicknames in ancient times, Chinese Qigong boasts a long history. It is not only a good way for people to cure illnesses, build up health, deter aging and prolong life, but also a key to exploring the mysteries of human physical science in contemporary time.

Qigong, a self-practice exercise aiming at refining *qi*, requires practitioners to exert subjective initiative to shape both the body and the spirit. As a comprehensive exercise, it is an initiative process of self-adjustment which plays the role of self-reliance, self-repair, self-regulation and self-building.

In Qigong exercise, *qi* is also known as genuine *qi*. In the view of TCM, it includes congenital *qi* and acquired *qi*. Inherited from parents, congenital *qi* is the primary substance, the basis for the formation of the embryo, and the elementary substance active for human body to maintain the physiological functions of tissues and organs. Acquired *qi* is the air we breathe and the refined food essence generated by the nutrients digested and absorbed by the *zangfu* organs to maintain man's life activities.

Interdependent and interacting, congenital *qi* and acquired *qi* constitute the genuine *qi* indispensable for man's life activities, the former being the basis and the motive force, and the latter the substantial source constantly nourishing and replenishing the body for all kinds of motivation.

Genuine *qi* accumulates and flows throughout the body following certain

This piece of jade unearthed of the Warring States bears the earliest inscription that tells how *qi* should be operated.

laws and paths. Meridians and collaterals are the passages for its circulation and transportation. Hence, to refine *qi* is to transport *qi* along the channels so that it can reach the internal *zangfu* organs, limbs and bones, to provide sufficient energy to body tissues, activate metabolism and strengthen physiological functions of human body.

"*Qi*" as in Qigong is a special and objective life phenomenon. "*Gong*," namely "*kungfu*," has a broader range of connotations, such as the duration, quality, methods, achievements, and skills, etc. To sum up, the practice that makes genuine *qi* flow smoothly and exuberantly in human body is the true meaning of "*gong*."

The duration of the exercise of Qigong reflects the will and determination of the practitioners. Qigong exercise needs persistence and perseverance; otherwise it is difficult to achieve success.

The quality of Qigong exercise is associated with the level of achievements. As sufficiency of genuine *qi* makes the body strong, to exercise is to cultivate and refine the genuine *qi*, which consists of the cultivation of mind-intention, regulation of breath and body constitution, the three elements in Qigong exercise.

Chinese Qigong can be roughly di-

Ancient Chinese picture illustrating Qigong acupoints

vided into five schools, namely, the Taoist, Buddhist, Confucius, Medical and Wushu schools. The Taoist Qigong gives consideration to both the spirit and body constitution, with equal emphasis on physical exercise and health care. The Buddhists mainly concentrate on spirit cultivation, leaving physical training out of account. It stresses "rectification of one's heart," "sincerity in one's thought" and "cultivation of a person." The Confucian Qigong strives for "mind-rest, concentration, stillness." The Medical Qigong is aimed at curing diseases for health care and longevity, which is represented by the vast majority of ancient medical practitioners who are simultaneously Qigong masters. And Wushu Qigong emphasizes body training for the very effect in self-defense and fighting, which, while contributing to health care and longevity, is distinctively different from other health care Qigong schools. However, in various styles of Wushu Qigong, there are also some elements taken from Buddhism, with Taijiquan as a typical example. On the other hand, most hard-form Qigong exercises are derived from Wushu.

Though with various feathers, all Qigong exercises can be divided into three categories in terms of the practicing forms: the static, dynamic, and combined exercises. Whatever method is adopted, concentration is a prerequisite for achieving the desired result.

II Dantian (elixir field) and Commonly Used Acupoints in Qigong Exercises

Dantian in Qigong Exercises

Dantian refers to the points where genuine *qi* is accumulated and stored. There are three *dantian* points in the body. The upper *dantian* is located behind the *baihui* acupoint on the top of the head or, correspondingly, 3 *cun* behind *yintang* acupoint between the eyebrows. The middle *dantian* is behind the *shanzhong* acupoint between the nipples. The lower *dantian* refers to the region in the abdomen below the navel.

The instruction "centering mind-intention in *dantian*" in Qigong practice usually means concentrating on the lower *dantian*, for this region bears the closest relation to human body activities. It is the hub for the ascending, descending, entering and exiting of the genuine *qi*, and in the same time the origin of life, the base of *zangfu* organs, the root of the twelve meridians, the junction of *yin* and *yang*, the gate of respiration, and the interaction of water and fire, as well as the place for men to store vital essence and for women to nourish the fetus. Centering mind-intention in *dantian* in Qigong practice helps to cultivate *qi*, build up health and prevent disease.

Centering mind-intension in the upper *dantian* is beneficial to patients with *qi* deficiency and subsidence, wind cold syndrome, cerebral anemia or low blood pressure. But it is not suitable for people with flaming up of heart fire, liver-*yang* hyperactivity or hypertension. Concentrating on the middle *dantian* is applicable to such symptoms as *qi* insufficiency in the middle-energizer, abnormally heavy menstrual flow, or when the menstrual blood is light in color. However, great care should be given to application of this practice since it tends to trigger off symptoms like chest distress, hypochondriac pain, etc.

Commonly Used Acupoints in Qigong Exercises

1. *Baihui*, literally "Hundred Convergences," at the vertax of the head, in line on the sides with the ears. This acupoint sits on the crown of the head where the three *yang* meridians of hand and foot and *Du* meridian as well as the body's *yang* energy naturally converge, hence the name. It is a crucial acupoint for acupoint-pointing therapy and massage. Settling the mind in this point can cure such symptoms as headache, dizziness, dazzle, amnesia, pavor or severe palpitation, prolapse of rectum, enuresis, gastroptosis, etc. (Fig 3-2-1)

2. *Tianting* (Middle Forehead), midpoint between *yintang* (see below) and forehead hair border. It is important for refining *qi* and curing mental diseases like amnesia, pavor, etc. (Fig 3-2-2)

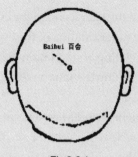

Fig 3-2-1

3. *Yintang* (Glabella), midpoint between the two medial ends of the eyebrow, used to treat headache, dizziness and other mental diseases. (Fig 3-2-2)

4. *Chengjiang* (Saliva Receiving), at the center of the mentolabial groove directly below the lower lip. Settling mind in this point can treat symptoms like fluid deficiency in practice, consumptive thirst and eye-mouth deviation. (Fig 3-2-2)

5. *Taiyang* (Supreme *Yang*), in the depression posterior to the midpoint

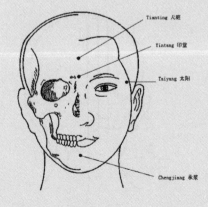

Fig 3-2-2

between the lateral end of the eyebrow and the outer canthus of the eye, used for alleviating *qi* stagnation, headache and rectifying deviation with Qigong. (Fig 3-2-2)

6. *Fengfu* (Wind Mansion), at *yuzhen* (jade occiput) pass, 1 *cun* directly above the midpoint of the posterior hairline, directly below the external occipital protuberance, in the depression between musculus trapezius of both sides. As the key path for the transportation of *qi* through *Ren* and *Du* meridians, its main effects lie in the cure of wind cold or disturbance of *qi* activity. (Fig 3-2-3)

7. *Fengchi* (Wind Pond), in a depression between sternocleidomastoid and the upper extreme of musculus trapezius of both sides, at the same level with *fengfu* acupoint. It is the gateway through which wind evil impairs the brain. Its massage pointing is for the

treatment of neck and back pain, feeling of obstruction in the ear and febrile disease without perspiration. (Fig 3-2-3)

8. *Queqiao* (Magpie Bridge), connecting parts of *Du* and *Ren* meridians and the major passage of *qi* circulation. Pushing tongue against palate while practicing is called "passing the magpie bridge."

9. *Tiantu* (Sky Prominence), at the notch in the superior aspect of the suprasternal fossa. As the highest point in the thoracic cavity, it is effective to smooth the flow of *qi*, assist expectoration and dispel stasis/ inability to swallow. (Fig 3-2-4)

10. *Shanzhong* (Middle Chest), in the middle level with the nipples of the beasts. As the converging point of *qi*, it plays an important role in refining and guiding *qi* and can cure *qifen* syndrome by external-*qi*-dilivery therapy. (Fig 3-2-4)

11. *Shenque* (Navel), in the center of the navel. This acupoint houses the acquired *qi* and stores the congenital *qi* hence contributing to the treatment of congenital and acquired diseases, and closely relating to the cultivation and accumulation, circulation and delivery of *qi*. (Fig 3-2-4)

12. *Huiyin* (Meeting of *Yin*), in the center of the perineum, meeting point on the *Ren* meridian with the *Du* and

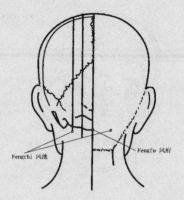

Fengchi 风池   Fengfu 风府

Fig 3-2-3

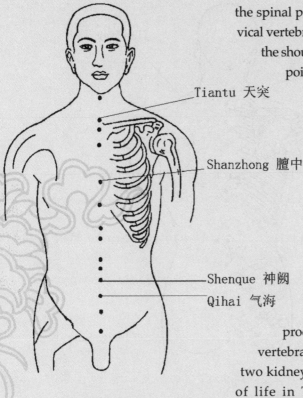

Tiantu 天突

Shanzhong 膻中

Shenque 神阙
Qihai 气海

Fig 3-2-4

the spinal process of the seventh cervical vertebra, almost at the level with the shoulders. As the convergence point of all *yang* meridians, it is regulated whenever *Yin Yang* imbalance occurs. Furthermore, as the most sensitive acupoint to the exterior *qi*, it is first regulated if *qi* in *Du* meridian needs to be guided. (Fig 3-2-6)

15. *Mingmen* (Life Gate), on the lower back, below the spinal process of the second lumbar vertebra. The region between the two kidneys is regarded as the gate of life in TCM, hence the name "*Mingmen*." It is closely related to the kidney. Sufficiency of kidney *qi* helps enhance health; stagnation of kidney *qi* leads to lumbago and soreness in the kidney region. Hyperactivities of fire from the gate of life caused by deficiency of kidney *qi* result in such syndromes as spermatorrhea, impotence,

Chong meridians. Beating in this region while practicing is triggered by the functioning of *qi* in the *Ren*, *Du* and *Chong* meridians. (Fig 3-2-5)

13. *Jianjin* (Shoulder Well), at the highest point of the shoulder, meeting point on the Gallbladder Meridian of Foot-Shaoyang with the Triple Energizer and Stomach meridians. This acupoint guides and regulates the functioning of *qi* all over the body pain and rigidity of the neck, arm and the lower limbs. (Fig 3-2-6)

14. *Dazhui* (Great Hammer), below

Huiyin 会阴

Fig 3-2-5

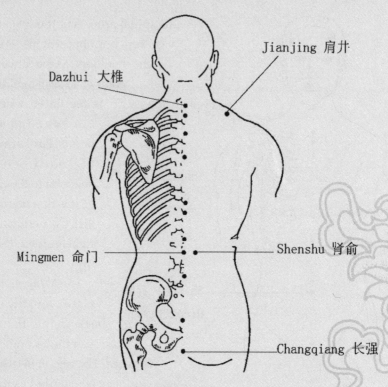

Fig 3-2-6

cloudy urine, and intestinal wind. It is the main acupoint to refining primordial *qi*, rectifying deviation and guiding. (Fig 3-2-6)

16. *Changqiang* (Long Strong), midway between the tip of the coccyx and the anus, locating the point in prone position. It is efficient for refining, guiding, regulating *qi*, and curing pain in the lower back, mania, epilepsy, diarrhea, constipation, five kinds of stranguria and seminal emission. (Fig 3-2-6)

17. *Sanguan* (Three Passes), *Weilü*, *Jiaji* and *Yuzhen*, of the *Du* meridian

where the *qi* can not easily go through. *Weilü* is another name of *changqiang* point; *jiaji* is located on both sides of *mingmen*; *yuzhen* is located below the occipital bone.

18. *Shenshu* (Kidney Shu), 1.5 *cun* lateral to the lower border of the spinal process of the second lumbar vertebra. Indications: deficiency of the kidney, deafness, lumbago, nocturnal emission, involuntary emission, irregular menstruation, etc. (Fig 3-2-6)

19. *Quchi* (Pool at the Bend), when the elbow is flexed, the point is in the depression at the lateral end of the

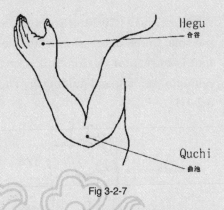

Fig 3-2-7

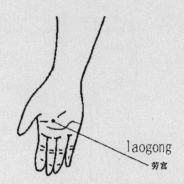

Fig 3-2-8

transverse cubital crease. Indications: dizziness, pain, inflammation and atorphy of the upper limbs. (Fig 3-2-7)

20. *Hegu* (Union Valley), on the dorsum of the hand, between the first and second metacarpal bones, approximately in the middle of the second metacarpal bone on the radial side. Indications: toothache, headache, fever, etc. (Fig 3-2-7)

21. *Laogong* (Palace of Toil), on the transverse crease of the palm, between the second and third metacarpal bones, key point for exiting and regulating *qi*. (Fig 3-2-8)

22. *Weizhong* (Bend Middle), midpoint of the transverse crease of the popliteal fossa, between the tendons of biceps femoris and semitendinosus. Indications: low back pain and pain of the lower extremities. (Fig 3-2-9)

23. *Chengshan* (Mountain Support), in the pointed depression below gastrocnemius on the posterior leg.

Indications: lower back pain and spasm of the gastrocnemius. (Fig 3-2-9)

24. *Zusanli* (Leg Three Li), 3 *cun* below the lower border of the petalla, one finger-breadth from the anterior crest of the tibia. Indications: abdominal pain, dizziness, cold and numbness of the lower extremities. (Fig 3-2-10)

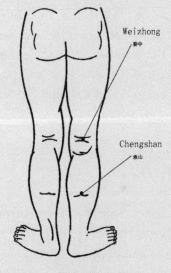

Fig 3-2-9

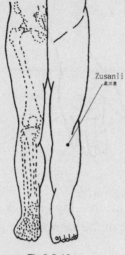

Fig 3-2-10

25. *Yongquan* (Gushing Spring), on the sole, in the depression when the foot is in plantar flexion. It is a key point for refining and guiding *qi*. (Fig 3-2-11)

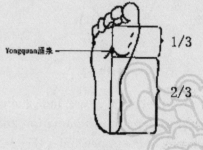

Fig 3-2-11

III Fundamentals, Essentials and Methods in the exercise of Qigong

Schools of Qigong exercise are various and so are the methods of exercising and their requirements. Whatever kind of schools to observe, fundamentals, essentials and methods in the exercise of Qigong must be followed. Otherwise, it is impossible to get good effects, and the learner may go astray.

prolonging life. Hence perseverance is needed to adhere to it and proceed despite such difficulties in the course as entering into tranquility, the reaction from arrival of *qi*, spontaneously moving and illusions. Only when one has set up confidence and had a correct understanding of possible deviations, can success be achieved.

Fundamentals of Qigong Exercises

1. Set a definit aim and persevere to achieve it

The aim of practicing Qigong consists in strengthening physique and

2. Correctly understand the dialectical relationship between qi and mind-intention

In Qigong, *qi* refers to the genuine *qi* in human body, while mind-intention means human's mental state, feelings and emotions. Practicing Qigong is to refine both *qi* and mind-intention. Without functions of mind-intention, the inner *qi* can't be well accumulated, stored and circulated, and one will never be successful. The exercise of Qigong should obey the objective laws that prescribe *qi* as fundamental and mind-intention as predominant, because the function and circulation of inner *qi* are regular and formed in the process of exercising. Roles of mind-intention can only be exerted on the basis of *qi*, and so exercising methods like using mind-intention to lead *qi* while solely pursuing the circle of *qi* around the meridians is liable to deviations. Therefore, the dominant role of mind-intention can only be played on the basis of following *qi*.

Mind-intention is needed when exercising Qigong but never too much, for otherwise it is not helpful for relaxation or entering into tranquility; instead, it may be liable to flatulence, suffocation and *qi* impairment. Refining mind-intention requires it to reside in intangibility and vice versa. When the exercise of Qigong has reached a considerable degree, the weaker the mind-intention is, the better the results, so as to achieve the realm of tranquility and nihility. In the mean time, one also should prevent loss of mind-intention, keeping in mind that one is exercising Qigong, so as to avoid lethargy and loss of control.

Refining *qi* requires not only holding acupoints but also promoting the flow of *qi*. Merely holding but not circulating may lead to accumulated suffocation, and circulating without holding to consumption of *qi*, which affects the accumulation and storage of inner *qi* in *dantian*. Only by combining the two can the genuine *qi* return to the root, and the inner *qi* exercised fully and circulated through meridians automatically. Hence, *qi* is guided by mind-intention to play the role of self-adjustment, health building and disease elimination.

3. Doing what comes naturally and gradually

In the process of Qigong exercise, different effects can be naturally achieved in different stages, and so excessively intentional pursuit must be avoided. Because of the individual difference, Qigong practitioners should choose methods suitable for themselves, instead of following stereotyped rules. In exercise, it is beneficial to keep an optimistic attitude and temperate amount of work. For under-conditioned patients, some effects can be achieved gradually if they stick to their exercise and supplement it with medication, doing it naturally as appropriate to their capacities.

Essentials of Qigong Exercise

1. Relaxing the body and spirit naturally

When practicing Qigong, relaxation should be both physical and mental. Usually, the body can be really relaxed as long as the spirit relaxes. However, relaxation does not mean slackness or inattentiveness. It should be just right and effective when you just feel comfortable. The static state means the calmness of spiritual activities when exercising. Entering into this state does not mean absolute stillness. The best condition is "stillness in motion and motion in stillness." Such a motion is carried on when the brain is in the state of being relatively calm. This is a process of eliminating fatigue and reserving energy and a special state of calmness while being awake in consciousness, which is different from natural sleep and repose. Relaxation and stillness is complementary and can promote each other. Being natural refers to the fact that all the gestures, breathing and intentions must be carried out naturally.

2. Mind-intension and *qi* going together

Qigong practitioners use their mind-intension activities to influence breathing and the circulation of genuine *qi*, making breathing slowly go on according to mind-intension activities, evenly and deeply. Meanwhile, it must be combined with relaxing, coming to stillness, circulating *qi*, and conserving mind-intention, so as to accumulate and activate the circulation of genuine *qi*.

3. Combination of motion and rest

Motion consists in body motion and the inner motion of breath. Similarly, rest refers to the rest of body and that of spirit. The essence of Qigong is to promote the physiological function to regulate body activities and restore health by balancing *yin* and *yang*, coordinating *qi* and blood, opening meridians and collaterals, cultivating genuine *qi*, and dispelling diseases and evils. Rest, especially the rest of spirit, is the precondition of Qigong exercise and determines the realization of the function of motion. Therefore, while choosing the appropriate practicing methods in accordance with personal conditions, one should combine motion and rest.

4. Empty in the upper parts and full in the lower parts

Qigong exercise underscores emptiness in the chest (the part above navel) and fullness in the abdomen (the part below navel), which can only be achieved by settling one's *qi* in the abdominal *dantian*. Qigong practitioners believe that fullness in the lower parts is the basis of exercise. Thus lowering one's *qi* down and centering mind in the *dantian* can prevent such signs and symptoms as top-heavy feeling and unstable paces induced by overabundance in the upper parts and deficiency in the lower parts. Emptiness in the upper parts, on the contrary, leads to a clear head, sharp sense, stable pace and inexhaustible vigor.

5. Combining exercise with nourishment

Progress can be made in Qigong practice only by combining exercise with nourishment and advancing in a gradual way. Over-exercise, over-running of *qi* or settling mind with extra effort is not appropriate for those with a weak constitution or chronic diseases, for it will harm both *qi* and spirit and induce breathing obstruction. Therefore, nourishment must be emphasized when Qigong exercise has progressed to a considerable extent. Thereupon, no mind-settlement or the flow of *qi* should be practiced. Mind-intention should be

gently placed in the *dantian* so as to accumulate congenital *qi*, nourish genuine *qi*. Constant efforts and long-term practice will naturally lead to a state of sufficient *qi* and abundant spirit, which is to be regarded as a success.

Basic Methods in Qigong Exercise

1. Regulating the body (Posture)

Qigong exercise requires the regulation of the postures in the first place. Accurate postures are the prerequisite of smooth breathing and spirit relaxing. Different postures have different physiological characters and certain therapeutic functions. Commonly used postures include: regular sitting, leg-crossing, single leg-crossing, supine lying, lateral recumbent lying, standing, walking, ect.

(1) Regular Sitting Posture

Sit up straight on a square chair with feet flat on the ground (The height of the chair shall ensure your thighs and torso to form a right angle. So are your thighs and shanks when bending knees.), knees shoulder-width apart, hands naturally resting on knees or thighs, chin drawn slightly inward, shoulders eased and chest relaxed, eyes and mouth slightly shut, tip of tongue pushed against palate, and smile on face. (Fig 3-3-1)

(2) Leg-Crossing Posture

Sit up straight on the plank bed with legs crossed, hands on knees or held tightly on lower abdomen (hands overlapped with *hukou* (part of a hand, between thumb and index finger) pushed against each other, right thumb pinching the transverse striation near the root of left ring finger and the other four fingers clinging to the back of left hand, fingertips of left thumb and middle finger pinched). Postures of the head, the upper part of the body, and the upper limbs are the same as in Fig 3-3-2.

(3) Single Leg-Crossing

Half-lotus sitting posture is mostly the same with full-lotus posture. The difference is that only one foot (either left or right) needs to be put on the thigh (right or left). (Fig 3-3-3)

(4) Supine Lying Posture

Lie bolstered up like a slope on the plank bed with legs straight, hands on sides of legs, head acting as in regular sitting posture. (Fig 3-3-4)

(5) Lateral Recumbent Lying Posture

Lie on your side on bed with head leveled up by a pillow. Keep torso straight and neck a little forward. Bend the upper leg and place it on the top

Fig 3-3-1

Fig 3-3-2

Fig 3-3-3

Fig 3-3-4

Fig 3-3-5

Fig 3-3-6

Fig 3-3-7

Fig 3-3-8

Fig 3-3-9

of the naturally unbent nether leg. Place upper hand on hip with palm facing downward and nether hand on the pillow with palm facing upward about two inches in distance from head. Other requirements are the same with those of supine posture. Right lateral position is in common use. (Fig 3-3-5)

(6) Standing Posture

Stand upright with feet shoulder-width apart, head and neck erect, chin drawn slightly inward, chest relaxed and back extended, knees bent and marrow eased, eyes looking straight ahead or slightly shut, arms forming a circle in front of chest, fingers naturally separated and slightly bent like holding a ball with palms facing each other and finger tips being about 30cm in distance, mouth naturally shut and tip of tongue pushed against palate, and smile on face. (Fig 3-3-6)

Standing posture can be classified into high, middle, low postures according to the bending levels of knees, and into natural style (Fig 3-3-7), push-down style (Fig 3-3-8), *fochang* style (Fig 3-3-9) and three-circle style according to different postures of the arms.

(7) Walking Posture

After standing still for two to three minutes, step forward with left foot, heel landing first, torso and hands swung rightward, nose inhaling and mouth exhaling. After left foot landing steadily on the ground, step forward with right foot, heel landing first, torso and hands swung leftward, nose inhaling and mouth exhaling. Keep walking this way for about half an hour.

2. Regulating the mind

The key point of regulating the mind in Qigong exercise is to concentrate your mind and exclude distracting thoughts through mind-intention, so as to enter into stillness and emptiness. This is the basic *kungfu* of Qigong as well as the key to the accomplishment of its exercise, for the effect is determined by the degree of stillness. Entering into stillness is usually hard for beginners. Commonly-used methods include:

(1) Mind Concentration

Highly concentrate your mind on a certain part of body, an acupoint or even a scene. Usually you can center mind in *dantian* or *qihai* acupoint (one inch and five *cun* below the navel). Don't pay too much attention to the process of mind concentration. Relax yourself and do it naturally.

(2) Breath-Following

Center mind on breath. Concentrate on the abdominal respiration rather than controlling it with mind, so as to achieve the unity of will and *qi* and to enter into stillness.

(3) Breath-Counting

Count your breath quietly while practicing Qigong. Keep counting until your ears hear nothing, eyes see nothing and mind cares nothing, hence entering into stillness naturally.

(4) Silent-Reading

Read a simple sentence or word silently. For instance, read "relax" in manner of pronouncing one syllable while inhaling and another while exhaling. Gradually you will discard all thoughts, be carefree and enter into stillness.

(5) Listen-to-Breath

Listen your breathing. It would be better if no sound can be heard. But you should imagine its possibility and try hard to listen, to help enter into stillness.

(6) Meditating

Try to see a certain part of body or a scene with mind-intention while practicing Qigong, so as to enter into self-induced stillness.

3. Regulating breath

This refers to the regulation and exercise of breathing. As an important link in *qi*-refining and the chief method to store, mobilize and circulate genuine *qi* in human body, it helps regulate *qi* and blood, massage internal organs from within the body, tranquillize the mind and relax. Commonly-adopted types of breathing include:

(1) Natural Breathing

Breathe naturally without using mind-intention.

(2) Abdominal Breathing

Inhale with the diaphragm going downward, the abdomen protruding outward. Exhale with the diaphragm going upward and the abdomen being drawn inward.

(3) Reverse Abdominal Breathing

Opposite to abdominal breathing, i.e. inhale with abdomen drawn inward and exhale with abdomen protruding outward.

(4) Breath-Holding

Hold breath for a while between each inhale and exhale.

(5) Nasal and Oral Breathing

Inhale with nose and exhale with mouth.

(6) Minor *Qi*-Circulation Breathing

While inhaling, mind-intention goes from *baihui* to *shanzhong*, lower *dantian* and ends at *huiyin* acupoint. While exhaling, mind-intention goes from *huiyin* to *weigu*, *jiaji*, *yuzhen* and ends at *baihui* acupoint. This type of breathing—mind-intension and *qi* go along *Ren* and *Du* meridians while

breathing with nose—is also called ventilation through *Ren* and *Du* meridians.

(7) Down-to-Heel Breathing

Breathe deeply so that *qi*, combined with mind concentration, can be guided to *yongquan* acupoint in the arch of your feet.

(8) Reading Silently While Breathing

Read silently while exhaling to exercise breathing.

(9) Genuine Breathing

Though it seems that breathing has stopped, actually it continues through bellybutton with *qi* whirling and vibrating in your abdomen, hence another name as "fetus breathing." This is an advanced stage in *kungfu*.

(10) Latent Breathing

This is an advanced type of breathing with long-time, subtle, even breaths and no distinct feelings of breathing itself. It is a master-level breathing method.

(11) Open-Close Breathing

Also called "body breathing," referring to an exercise based on "fetus breathing." For instance, imagining that the pores all over the body are opening and closing with the proceeding of breathing and the penetration of breath. Another name is "pore breathing."

IV Effects and Points for Attention in Qigong Exercises

Spontaneous Effects in Qigong Exercise

Some particular effects will come up with the progress of Qigong exercise, including normal effects and abnormal ones. Generally speaking, normal effects will emerge if it is properly practiced and the precautions are seriously noticed; on the other hand, if the practitioners exercise improperly, advance rashly, or deliberately pursue some particular effect against the natural practice, abnormal effects will appear. To conclude, the effects are closely related to such factors as the physical condition of the practitioner, his/her comprehension of the common knowledge of Qigong, the environment and the progress of exercise. Therefore, specific analysis of the spontaneous effects needs to be made.

1. Normal effects

(1) Feeling warm and perspiring slightly. Practitioner feels warm in his lower abdomen and limbs. With the progress of *kungfu*, the warm feeling can connect *Ren* and *Du* meridians. Slight perspiration is recommended while heavy perspiration must be avoided.

(2) Saliva increasing. It can be slowly swallowed, which has a favorable effect on the digestive system.

(3) Practitioners feeling refreshed and vigorous. This feeling usually occurs after having practiced for 30 minutes and getting into deeper stillness, and will remain for quite a long time after the exercise.

(4) Sleep deepening. Practitioners can fall asleep quickly and deeply. It plays a positive role in eliminating fatigue and recovering physical fitness.

(5) Gastrointestinal motility speeding up and appetite increasing.

(6) Skin itching, muscle shivering and condyle cracking. Actually, they are all symbols of the energetic functioning of *qi* in the body of the practitioner, which usually appear at the end of the limbs, lumbosacral portion or the nape, and will disappear automatically. Slightly diverting attention can help relieve the feeling of this effect.

(7) Metabolism accelerating, saliva and sweat increase; fingernails, hair and beard growing faster during the period.

(8) Feeling comfortable and relaxed.

2. Abnormal effects

(1) Symptoms of dizziness, distention of head, headache, heaviness and tightness in the head. The main causes of these symptoms are nervousness, too much mind-intention, forced stillness and the tension building up in the practitioner. Correcting the wrong practicing methods or taking deep breath can help relieve and get rid of the symptoms.

(2) Symptoms of xerostomia, syrigmus and dry eyes. Physical weakness and excessively frequent sex, which alter coordination between the heart and kidneys, imbalance between *yin* and *yang* and ascent of deficient *yang* are the main causes. To prevent and cure these symptoms, practitioners should strictly control the frequency of sex activity and don't resume the exercise until one or two days after sex.

(3) Fullness and oppression in the chest and abdomen, and breathing difficulty. The causes are too much attention to breathing, deliberate pursuit of deep and long breath, or inabil-

Patients are practicing Qigong to cure diseases under the guidance of the doctor in Chongqing, 1958.

ity to relax the upper part of the body. Thus, these effects can be eliminated if the practitioner advances gradually, takes natural and soft breath, and conforms to the principle of "combination of exercise and nourishment."

(4) Symptoms of short and shallow breathing and abdominal distention. The main cause is that the practitioner forces himself to breathe deeply and is anxious to change natural breathing into abdominal breathing, thus causing weariness of the respiratory muscle. Suggestion for addressing this problem is to advance gradually in the course and frequently practice.

(5) Symptoms of tachycardia and pain in chest and hypochondrium. These symptoms may be triggered by straightening the chest or bending the waist excessively, being nervous, holding one's breath for too long or reciting too many numbers in the course of exercise. They will recover automatically as long as the practitioner relaxes thoroughly and pays less attention to breathing.

(6) Vibration of the body. The practitioner usually feels slight vibration though the body actually does not shake or shiver. This feeling arises due to the change of the functioning of *qi* inside the body. Different methods shall be adopted to deal with in vari-

ous situations. For instance, if the practitioner is practicing with eyes closed, he can slightly open eyes, or remind himself of relaxation. Body vibration is sometimes good but should not be allowed to develop while doing some static exercises. However, it is necessary while doing motion-and-stillness-combined exercise and should be practiced according to the concrete rules.

(7) Feeling cold or hot. Hot weather, wearing too much clothing, being overfull, eating too much meat, sufficient *jing* and internal heat lead to hot feeling while low temperature, wearing too little clothing, feeling hungry, frequent spermatorrhea, serious disease and anemia account for cold feeling. Therefore, Qigong exercise should be avoided when the practitioner is too full or hungry. Choosing light diet, breathing in fresh air, wearing suitable closes, avoiding too much mind and irritation can remove such a negative effect.

Points for Attention in Qigong Exercise

1. Have a correct understanding of Qigong exercise, realize the aim of it, exert subjective initiative, advance gradually in a right way, and be studious and hard-working.

2. Beginners should practice under the guidance of an experienced

Two foreign girls are practicing healthcare Qigong Five-Animal Play with the teacher in Xuchang, Henan Province.

Qigong master, choose the appropriate exercise, and avoid being inconstant and changeable; otherwise, the normal effects of Qigong exercise will be influenced.

3. Duration of exercise varies among different people and no uniform pattern should be followed. It's appropriate for patients to practice three times a day, about 30 minutes each time and gradually increase the time; healthy practitioners can arrange it based on their personal conditions, generally one to three times a day; the duration and intensity should be determined by the physical condition of the practitioner, assuring that he/she has no feeling of exhaustion after the exercise.

4. Take a quiet place with fresh air as the exercise ground. Avoid unexpected noises, strong light, or chilly wind. Ensure good ventilation while practicing indoors.

5. Make full preparation before exercise. Relieve yourself, wear suitable and loose-fitting clothes, and drink a small quantity of warm water if thirsty.

6. Carry out the exercise of "breath

regulation." Whatever method is adopted, you need to transform to natural breathing every 20 minutes to avoid weariness and paralysis of the respiratory muscle and the risk of being choked. Do remember the principle of being natural.

7. Do not practice when over-excited, upset, exhausted, or too full or hungry.

8. For practitioners who are feeble or have such diseases as hypertension, heart disease, pulmonary tuberculosis, hepatitis, kidney disease and neurasthenia, etc., sex life must be forbidden for a period of time in the course of the exercise and be checked after recovery.

9. Qigong exercise is not suitable for critical patients and special patients like the mentally abnormal, paranoiac, or radicals. However, they can choose to do exercises other than those requiring mind-intension.

10. Women in their menstrual period should not practice too long or take high-tempo and overburdened exercises. While carrying out static exercises, they should not center mind in lower *dantian* or guide too much intention to the lower part of the body. However, it is all right to concentrate on *shanzhong* acupoint.

11. Do remember the "three stables" —stable in the opening form, stable during the exercise and stable in the closing form.

12. Arrange life routines in a scientific way. Regulate daily life and well appropriate exercise, work and study, so as to achieve a better effect.

Chapter Four
Taijiquan Exercises

I 24 Form Taijiquan

Direction 1: In the illustrations, the paths of the movements to be executed are indicated by arrows drawn in solid lines for the right hand and foot, and dotted lines for the left hand and foot.

Direction 2: Directions are given in term of the 12 hours of feet clock.

Form 1 Opening Form

l) Stand upright with feet shoulder-width apart, toes pointing forward, arms hanging naturally at sides, hands relaxed and gently touching the side of leg. Look straight ahead. (Fig 4-1-1)

Key points: Keep head and neck erect, with chin drawn slightly inward. Do not protrude chest or draw in abdomen.

2) Raise arms gradually forward to shoulder height, palms facing down. (Figs 4-1-2, 4-1-3)

3) Bend knees as you press palms down gently, with elbows dropping towards knees. Look straight ahead. (Fig 4-1-4)

Key Points: Keep torso erect and hold shoulders and elbows down, with fingers slightly curved, body weight equally distributed between legs. While bending knees, keep waist relaxed and buttocks slightly pulled in. The lowering of arms should be in line with the bending of knees.

| Fig 4-1-1 | Fig 4-1-2 | Fig 4-1-3 | Fig 4-1-4 |

Form 2 Zuo You Ye Ma Fen Zong: Parting the Wild Horse's Mane—Parting One's Hands Slantingly for Holding or Striking.

Fig 4-1-5

Fig 4-1-6

1) With torso turning slightly to the right (1 o'clock) and weight shifted onto right leg, raise right hand until forearm comes parallel to, but slightly in front of the right side of the chest, while the left hand moves in a downward arc until it comes underneath of the right hand, palms facing each other as if holding a ball between two hands (henceforth referred to as "hold-ball gesture"). Draw left foot to the inner side of right foot, toes on floor. Look at right hand. (Figs 4-1-5, 4-1-6)

Fig 4-1-7

2) Turn body to the left (10 o'clock) as left foot takes a step towards 8–9 o'clock. Bend knee and shift weight onto left leg, while straightening right leg with whole foot on floor for a left "bow stance." As you turn body, raise left hand to eye level with palm facing obliquely up and elbow slightly bending; at the same time lower right hand to the side of right hip with palm facing down and fingers pointing forward. Look at left hand. (Figs 4-1-7, 4-1-8, 4-1-9)

Fig 4-1-8

3) "Sit back" slowly; move torso backward as if you are ready to take a seat and shift weight onto right leg, raising toes of left foot slightly and

Fig 4-1-9

turning them outward before placing whole foot on floor. Then bend left leg and turn body to the left, shifting weight onto left leg and making a hold-ball gesture in front of left part of chest, this time with the left hand on top. Then move right foot to the inner side of left foot, with toes touching the floor. Look at left hand. (Figs 4-1-10, 4-1-11, 4-1-12)

4) Take a right bow stance by moving right foot a step towards 9 o'clock, straightening left leg with whole foot on floor and bending right leg. At the same time, with body turning slightly to the right, gradually raise right hand to eye level with palm facing obliquely upward and elbow bending slightly; press left hand down to the side of left hip, palm down. Look at right hand. (Figs 4-1-13, 4-1-14)

5) Repeat movements in 3), reversing "right" and "left." (Figs 4-1-15, 4-1-16, 4-1-17)

6) Repeat movements in 4), reversing "right" and "left." (Figs 4-1-18, 4-1-19)

Key points: Hold torso erect and keep chest relaxed. Move arms in an arc way without stretching them when you separate hands. Use waist as the axis when body turns. The movements in taking a bow stance and separating hands must be smooth and synchronized in tempo. When taking a bow

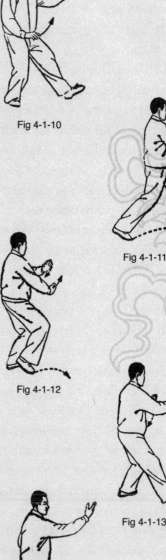

Fig 4-1-10

Fig 4-1-11

Fig 4-1-12

Fig 4-1-13

Fig 4-1-14

Fig 4-1-15

Fig 4-1-16

Fig 4-1-17

Fig 4-1-18

Fig 4-1-19

stance, place front foot slowly in position, with the heel coming down first. The knee of front leg should not be bent beyond toes, while rear leg should be kept straight, forming an angle of 45 degrees to the floor. There should be a distance of 10-30 cm between heels. Face 9 o'clock in final position.

Form 3 Bai He Liang Chi: White Crane Spreading Its Wings—Extending One's Arms Symmetrically or Slantingly for Defending

1) With torso turning slightly to the left (8 o'clock), the right hand moves upward as the left hand moves downward. Make a hold-ball gesture in front of left part of chest, left hand above. Look at left hand. (Fig 4-1-20)

2) Draw right foot half a step towards left foot and then sit back. Turn torso slightly to the right (10 o'clock), with weight being shifted onto right leg and eyes looking at right hand. Move left foot a bit forward, with toes on floor for a left "empty stance," with both legs bending slightly. At the same time, with torso turning slightly to the left (9 o'clock), raise right hand to the front of right temple, palm turns inward, while left hand moves down to the front of left hip, palm down. Look straight ahead. (Figs 4-1-21,

Fig 4-1-20

Fig 4-1-22

Fig 4-1-21

4-1-22)

Key points: Do not thrust chest forward. Arms should be rounded when they move up or down; weight transfer should be coordinated with the raising of right hand. Face 9 o'clock in final position.

Form 4 Zuo You Lou Xi Ao Bu: Brushing Knees and Twisting Steps

1) Turn torso slightly to the left (8 o'clock) as right hand moves down while left hand moves up. Then turn torso to the right (11 o'clock) as right hand circles past abdomen and up to ear level with arm slightly bending and palm facing obliquely upward. In the mean time, left hand moves in an upward-rightward-downward arc to the front of right part of chest, palm facing obliquely downward. Look at right hand. (Figs 4-1-23, 4-1-24, 4-1-25)

2) Turn torso to the left (9 o'clock) as left foot takes a step in the same direction for a left bow stance. At the same time, right hand draws leftward past right ear and, following body turn, pushes forward to nose level with palm facing forward. In the mean time, left hand circles around left knee to stop beside left hip, palm down. Look at fingers of right hand. (Figs 4-1-26, 4-1-27)

3) Sit back slowly with right knee bending, shifting weight onto right leg. Raise toes of left foot and turn them a bit outward before placing whole foot on floor. Then bend left leg slowly and turn body slightly to the left, shifting weight onto left leg. Bring right foot forward to the side of left foot, toes on floor. At the same time, turn left palm up and with elbow slightly bending, move left hands sideways and up to shoulder level. Right hand, following body turn, moves upward and then left-downward to the front of the left chest, palm facing

obliquely downward. Look at left hand. (Figs 4-1-28, 4-1-29, 4-1-30)

4) Repeat movements in 2), reversing "right" and "left." (Figs 4-1-31, 4-1-32)

5) Repeat movements in 3), reversing "right" and "left" . (Figs 4-1-33, 4-1-34, 4-1-35)

6) Repeat movements in 2). (Figs 4-1-36, 4-1-37)

Fig 4-1-23

Fig 4-1-24

Fig 4-1-25

Fig 4-1-26

Fig 4-1-27

Fig 4-1-28

Fig 4-1-29

Fig 4-1-30

Fig 4-1-31

Fig 4-1-32

Fig 4-1-33

Fig 4-1-35

Fig 4-1-37

Fig 4-1-34

Fig 4-1-36

Key points: Keep torso erect and waist relaxed and hold shoulders and elbow down while pushing palm forward. Movements, of palm should be in line with those of waist and legs. Keep a transverse distance of 30 cm between heels in bow stance. Face 9 o'clock in final position.

Form 5 Shou Hui Pi Pa: Playing the Lute

Move right foot half a step towards left heel. Sit back and turn torso slightly to the right (10-11 o'clock), shifting weight onto right leg. Raise left foot and place it slightly forward, heel coming down on floor and knee bending a little for a left empty stance. At the same time, raise left hand in an arc to nose level, with palm facing rightward and elbow slightly bending while moving right hand to the inside of left elbow, palm facing leftward. Look at forefingers of left hand. (Figs 4-1-38, 4-1-39, 4-1-40)

Key points: Body position should remain steady and natural, chest relaxed and shoulders and elbows held down. Movements in raising left hand should be moderately circular. In moving right foot half a step forward, place it slowly in position, toes coming down first. Weight transfer must be coordinated with the raising of left hand. Face 9 o'clock in final position.

| Fig 4-1-38 | Fig 4-1-39 | Fig 4-1-40 |

Form 6 Zuo You Dao Juan Gong: Stepping Back and Whirling Arms on Both Sides

1) Turn torso slightly to the right, moving right hand down in an arc past abdomen and then upward to shoulder level, palm up and arm slightly bending. Turn left palm up and place toes of left foot on floor. Look to the right first as body turns in that direction, and then turn to look at left hand. (Figs 4-1-41, 4-1-42)

2) Bend right arm and draw hand past right ear before pushing it out with palm facing forward while left

hand moves to waist side, palm up. At the same time, raise left foot slightly and take a curved step backward, place toes down first and then the whole foot slowly on floor with toes turning outward. Turn body slightly to the left and shift weight onto left leg for a right empty stance, with right foot pivoting on toes until it points directly ahead. Look at right hand. (Figs 4-1-43, 4-1-44)

3) Turn torso slightly to the left, carrying left hand sideways up to shoulder level, palm up, while right palm is turned up. Look to the left first as

| Fig 4-1-41 | Fig 4-1-42 | Fig 4-1-43 | Fig 4-1-44 |

body turns in that direction and then turn to look at right hand. (Fig 4-1-45)

4) Repeat movements in 2), reversing "right," and "left." (Figs 4-1-46, 4-1-47)

5) Repeat movements in 3), reversing "right," and "left." (Fig 4-1-48)

6) Repeat movements in 2). (Figs 4-1-49, 4-1-50)

7) Repeat movements in 3). (Fig 4-1-51)

8) Repeat movements in 2), reversing "right," and "left." (Figs 4-1-52, 4-1-53)

Fig 4-1-45

Fig 4-1-46

Fig 4-1-47

Fig 4-1-48

Fig 4-1-49

Fig 4-1-50

Fig 4-1-51

Fig 4-1-52

Fig 4-1-53

Key points: Hands should move in an arc way when they are being pushed out or drawn back. While pushing out hands, keep waist and hips relaxed. The turning of waist should be coordinated with hand movements. When stepping back, place toes down first and then slowly set the whole foot on floor. Simultaneously with body turn, point front foot directly ahead, pivoting on toes. When stepping back, the right foot should move a bit sideways so as to do next form. First look in the direction of body turn and then turn to look at the hand in front. Face 9 o'clock in final position.

Fig 4-1-54

Fig 4-1-55

Fig 4-1-56

Form 7 Zuo Lan Que Wei: Grasping the Peacock's Tail— Left Style Peng: Warding Off

1) Turn torso slightly to the right (11-12 o'clock), carrying right hand sideways up to shoulder level, palm up, while left palm is turned downward. Look at left hand. (Fig 4-1-54)

2) Turn body slightly to the right (12 o'clock) and make a hold-ball gesture in front of right part of chest, right hand above. At the same time, shift weight onto right leg and draw left foot to the side of right foot, toes on floor. Look at right hand. (Figs 4-1-55, 4-1-56)

3) Turn body slightly to the left, and take a step forward with left foot moving towards 9 o'clock for a left bow stance. Meanwhile, push out left forearm and back of hand to shoulder level as if to fend off a blow, while right hand drops slowly to the side of right hip, palm down. Look at left forearm. (Figs 4-1-57, 4-1-58)

Key points: Keep both arms rounded while pushing out one of them. The separation of hands, turning of waist and bending of leg should

Fig 4-1-57

Fig 4-1-58

Fig 4-1-59

Fig 4-1-60

Fig 4-1-61

Fig 4-1-62

be coordinated.

Lu: Rolling Back

4) Turn torso slightly to the left (9 o'clock) while extending left hand forward, palm down. Bring up right hand until it is below left forearm, palm up. Then turn torso slightly to the right while pulling both hands down in an arc way past abdomen—as if you are taking hold of an imaginary foe's elbow and wrist in order to pull back his hand and body—until right hand is extended sideways at shoulder level, palm up, and left forearm lies across chest, palm turned inward. At the same time, shift weight onto right leg. Look at right hand. (Figs 4-1-59, 4-1-60)

Key points: While pulling down hands, do not lean forward or protrude buttocks. Arms should follow the turning of waist and move in a circular path.

Ji: Pressing

5) Turn torso slightly to the left as you bend right arm and place right hand inside left wrist; turn torso further to 9 o'clock as you press both hands slowly forward, palms facing each other and keeping a distance of about 5 cm between them and left arm remaining rounded. Meanwhile, shift weight slowly onto left leg for a left bow stance. Look at left wrist. (Figs 4-1-61, 4-1-62)

Key points: Keep torso erect when pressing hands forward. The movement of hands must be coordinated with the turning of waist and the bending of front leg.

An: Pushing

6) Turn both palms downward as right hand passes over left wrist and moves forward and then to the right until it is on the same level with left

Fig 4-1-63

Fig 4-1-64

Fig 4-1-65

Fig 4-1-66

hand. Separate hands shoulder-width apart and draw them back to the front of abdomen, palms facing obliquely downward. At the same time, sit back and shift weight onto right leg which bends slightly, raising toes of left foot. Look straight ahead. (Figs 4-1-63, 4-1-64, 4-1-65)

7) Transfer weight slowly onto left leg while pushing palms in an upward-forward arc until wrists are as high as shoulder. At the same time, bend left leg for a left bow stance. Look straight ahead. Face 9 o'clock in final position. (Fig 4-1-66)

Key points: When pushing hands, it should go circle line and wrists keep as high as shoulders. The elbows bend slightly.

Form 8 You Lan Que Wei: Grasping the Peacock's Tail— Right Style

1) Sit back and turn torso to the right (12 o'clock), shifting weight onto right leg and turning toes of left foot inward. Move right hand in a horizontal way to the right and move downward past abdomen for a hold-ball gesture in front of left part of chest, left hand on top. Meanwhile, shift weight onto left leg and place right foot beside left foot, toes on floor. Look at left hand. (Figs 4-1-67, 4-1-68, 4-1-69, 4-1-70)

2) Repeat movements in 3)-7) under Form 7, reversing "right" and "left." (Figs 4-1-71, 4-1-72, 4-1-73, 4-1-74, 4-1-75, 4-1-76, 4-1-77, 4-1-78, 4-1-79, 4-1-80)

Key points: The Same as those for Form 7. Face 3 o'clock in final position.

Fig 4-1-67

Fig 4-1-68

Fig 4-1-69

Fig 4-1-70

Fig 4-1-71

Fig 4-1-72

Fig 4-1-73

Fig 4-1-74

Fig 4-1-75

Fig 4-1-76

Fig 4-1-77

Fig 4-1-78

Fig 4-1-79

Fig 4-1-80

Form 9 Dan Bian: Single Whip

1) Sit back and shift weight gradually onto left leg, turning toes of right foot inward. Meanwhile, turn body to the left (11 o'clock), carrying both hands leftward, left hand on top, until left arm is extended sideways at shoulder level, palm facing outward, and right hand is in front of left ribs, palm facing obliquely inward. Look at left hand. (Figs 4-1-81, 4-1-82)

2) Turn body to the right (1 o'clock), shifting weight gradually onto right leg and drawing left foot to the side of

right foot, toes on floor. At the same time, move right hand to the right-upward until arm is at shoulder level. With right palm now turning outward, bunch fingertips and turn them downward from wrist for a "hook hand," while left hand moves in an arc past abdomen up to the front of right shoulder, palm facing inward. Look at left hand. (Figs 4-1-83, 4-1-84)

3) Turn body to the left (10 o'clock) while left foot takes a step towards 8-9 o'clock for a left bow stance. While shifting weight onto left leg, turn left palm slowly outward as you push it

forward with fingertips at eye level and elbow slightly bending. Look at left hand. (Figs 4-1-85, 4-1-86)

Key points: Keep torso erect, waist relaxed and shoulders lowered. Left palm is turned outward slowly, not too abruptly, as hand pushes forward. All transitional movements must be well coordinated. Face 9 o'clock in final position, with right elbow slightly bending downward and left elbow just above left knee.

Fig 4-1-84

Fig 4-1-85

Fig 4-1-81

Fig 4-1-82

Fig 4-1-86

Fig 4-1-83

Form 10 Yun Shou: Waving Hands like Floating Clouds— Left Style

1) Shift weight onto right leg and turn body gradually to the right (1-2 o'clock), turning toes of left foot inward. At the same time, move left hand in an arc past abdomen to the front of right shoulder, palm turned obliquely inward, while right hand is opened, palm facing outward. Look at

left hand. (Figs 4-1-87, 4-1-88, 4-1-89)

2) Turn torso gradually to the left (10-11 o'clock), shifting weight onto left leg. At the same time, move left hand in an arc past face with palm turning slowly leftward, while right hand moves in an arc past abdomen up to the front of left shoulder with palm slowly turning obliquely inward. As right hand moves upward, bring right foot to the side of left foot so that they are parallel and 10-20 cm apart. Look at right hand. (Figs 4-1-90, 4-1-91)

3) Turn torso gradually to the right (l-2 o'clock), shifting weight onto right leg. At the same time, move right hand continuously to right side past face, palm turns slowly outward, while left hand moves in an arc past abdomen up to shoulder level with palm turning slowly and obliquely inward. As left hand moves upward, take a side step with left foot. Look at left hand. (Figs 4-1-92, 4-1-93, 4-1-94)

4) Repeat movements in 2), 3), and 2). (Figs 4-1-95, 4-1-96, 4-1-97, 4-1-98, 4-1-99, 4-1-100, 4-1-101)

Key points: Use your lumbar spine as the axis for body turns. Keep waist

Fig 4-1-87

Fig 4-1-88

Fig 4-1-89

Fig 4-1-90

Fig 4-1-91

and hips relaxed. Do not let your body rise and fall abruptly. Arm movements should be natural and circular and follow waist movements. Pace must be slow and even. Maintain a good balance when moving lower limbs. Eyes should follow the hand that is moving past face. Body in final position faces 10-11 o'clock.

Fig 4-1-92

Fig 4-1-93

Fig 4-1-94

Fig 4-1-95

Fig 4-1-96

Fig 4-1-97

Fig 4-1-98

Fig 4-1-99

Fig 4-1-100

Fig 4-1-101

Form 11 Dan Bian: Single Whip

1) Turn torso to the right (1 o'clock), moving right hand to right side for a hook hand while left hand moves in an arc past abdomen to the front of right shoulder with palm facing the face. Shift weight onto right leg, toes of left foot on floor. Look at left hand. (Figs 4-1-102, 4-1-103, 4-1-104)

2) Repeat movements in 3) under Form 9. (Figs 4-1-105, 4-1-106)

Key points: The same as those for Form 9.

Form 12 Gao-Tan-Ma: Patting the Horse on the Back

1) Draw right foot half a step forward and shift weight gradually onto right leg. Open right hand and turn up both palms, elbows slightly bend while body turns slightly to the right (10-11 o'clock), raising left heel gradually for a left empty stance. Look at left hand. (Fig 4-1-107)

2) Turn body slightly to the left (9 o'clock), pushing right palm forward past right ear, fingertips at eye level, while left hand moves to the front of left hip, palm up. At the same time, move left foot a bit forward, toes on floor. Look at right hand. (Fig 4-1-108)

Key points: Keep torso erect, shoulders lowered and right elbow slightly downward. Face 9 o'clock in final position.

Fig 4-1-102

Fig 4-1-103

Fig 4-1-104

Fig 4-1-105

Fig 4-1-106

Fig 4-1-107

Fig 4-1-108

Form 13 You-Deng-Jiao: Kicking with Right Heel

1) Turn torso slightly to the right (10 o'clock) and move left hand, palm up, to cross right hand at wrist as you pull left foot a bit backward, toes on floor. Then separate hands, and move both hands in a downward arc with palms turning obliquely downward. Meanwhile, raise left foot to take a step towards 8 o'clock for a left bow stance, toes turn slightly outward. Look straight ahead. (Figs 4-1-109, 4-1-110, 4-1-111)

2) Continue to move hands in a downward-inward-upward arc until wrists cross in front of chest, with right hand in front and both palms turning inward. At the same time, draw right foot to the side of left foot, toes on floor. Look forward to the right. (Fig 4-1-112)

3) Separate hands, turning torso slightly to 8 o'clock and extending both arms sideways at shoulder level with elbows slightly bending and palms turning outward. At the same time, raise right knee and thrust foot gradually towards 10 o'clock. Look at right hand. (Figs 4-1-113, 4-1-114)

Key points: Keep your balance. Wrists are at shoulder level when hands are separated. When kicking right foot, left leg is slightly bent and the kicking force should be focused on heel, with ankle buckling backward. The separation of hands should be in line with the kick. Right

Fig 4-1-109

Fig 4-1-110

Fig 4-1-111

Fig 4-1-112   Fig 4-1-113   Fig 4-1-114

arm is parallel with right leg. Face 9 o'clock in final position.

Form 14 Shuang Feng Guan Er: Striking the Opponent's Ears with Both Fists

1) Pull back right foot and keep thigh level. Move left hand in an arc way to the side of right hand in front of chest, both palms turn inward. Bring hands to both sides of right knee, palm up. Look straight ahead. (Figs 4-1-115, 4-1-116)

2) Set right foot slowly on the floor towards 10 o'clock, shifting weight onto right leg for a right bow stance. At the same time, lower hands to both sides and gradually clench fists; then move them backward with an inward rotation of the arms before moving them upward and forward for a pincer movement that ends at eye level with fists about 10-20 cm apart, knuckles pointing upward to the back. Look at right fist. (Figs 4-1-117, 4-1-118)

Key points: Hold head and neck erect. Keep waist and hips relaxed and fits loosely clenched. Keep shoulders and elbows lowered and arms rounded. Face 10 o'clock in final position.

Fig 4-1-115   Fig 4-1-116   Fig 4-1-117   Fig 4-1-118

Form 15　Zhuan Shen Zuo Deng Jiao: Kicking with Left Heel

1) Sit back with left knee bent and shift weight gradually onto left leg, turning body to the left (6 o'clock) with toes of right foot turning inward. Simultaneously, open both fists and separate hands in an upward arc, extending both arms sideways, palms facing outward. Look at left hand. (Figs 4-1-119, 4-1-120)

2) Shift weight onto right leg and draw left foot to the side of right foot, toes on floor. At the same time, move both hands in a downward-inward-upward arc until wrists cross in front of chest, with left hand in front and both palms facing inward. Look forward to the left. (Figs 4-1-121, 4-1-122)

3) Separate hands, extending both arms sideways at shoulder level, elbows slightly bent and palms facing outward Meanwhile, raise left knee and thrust foot gradually toward 4 o'clock. Look at left hand. (Figs 4-1-123, 4-1-124)

Key points: The same as those for Form 13, except that "right" and "left" are reversed. Face 4 o'clock in final position

Fig 4-1-119

Fig 4-1-120

Fig 4-1-121

Fig 4-1-122

Fig 4-1-123

Fig 4-1-124

Form 16 Zuo Xia Shi Du Li: Snake Creeping Down and Golden Rooster Standing on Left Leg

Snake Creeping Down

1) Pull back left foot, keeping thigh level. Turn torso to the right (7 o'clock). Hook right hand as you turn up left palm and move it in an arc past face to the front of right shoulder, turning it inward in the process. Look at right hand. (Figs 4-1-125, 4-1-126)

Fig 4-1-125

Fig 4-1-126

2) Turn torso to the left (4 o'clock), and squat down slowly on right leg, extending left leg low sideways towards 2-3 o'clock. Move left hand down and to the left along the inside of left leg towards left ankle, with palm turning outward. Look at left hand. (Figs 4-1-127, 4-1-128)

Fig 4-1-127

Key points: When crouching down, turn toes of right foot slightly outward and straighten left leg with toes turning slightly inward and both soles being flat on floor. Keep toes of left foot in line with right heel. Do not lean torso too much forward.

Fig 4-1-128

Golden Rooster Standing on Left Leg

3) Turn toes of left foot outward and those of right foot inward; straighten right leg and bend left leg onto which weight is shifted. Turn torso slightly to the left (3 o'clock) as you rise up slowly in a forward movement. At the same time, move left arm continuously to the front, palm facing right, while right hand drops behind the back still in the form of a hook, with bunched fingertips pointing backward. Look at left hand. (Fig 4-1-129)

Fig 4-1-129

Fig 4-1-131

Fig 4-1-130

Form 17 You Xia Shi Du Li: Snake Creeping Down and Golden Rooster Standing on Right Leg

1) Put right foot down in front of left foot, toes on floor, Turn body to the left (12 o'clock), pivoting on toes of left foot. At the same time, raise left hand sideways to shoulder level and turn it into a hook while right hand, following body turn, moves in an arc to the front of left shoulder with fingers pointing up. Look at left hand. (Figs 4-1-132, 4-1-133)

2) Repeat movements in2)-4) under Form 16, reversing "right" and "left" and changing the clock directions of movements accordingly. (Figs 4-1-134, 4-1-135, 4-1-136, 4-1-137, 4-1-138)

Key points: Raise right foot slightly before crouching down and stretching

4) Raise right knee slowly until level with hip as right hand opens into palm and swings to the front past outside of right leg, elbow bends just over right knee, right fingers pointing up and palm facing left. Move left hand down to the side of left hip, palm down. Look at right hand. (Figs 4-1-130, 4-1-131)

Key points: Keep torso upright. Bend the supporting leg slightly. Toes of the raised leg should point naturally downward. Face 3 o'clock in final position.

Fig 4-1-132

Fig 4-1-133

Fig 4-1-134

Fig 4-1-135

Fig 4-1-136

Fig 4-1-137

Fig 4-1-138

right leg sideways. Other points are the same with those for Form 16, except that "right" and "left" are reversed. Face 3 o'clock in final position.

Form 18 Zuo You Chuan Suo: Working at Shuttles on Both Sides

1) Turn body to the left (1 o'clock) as you set left foot on floor in front of right foot, toes turn outward. With right heel slightly raised, bend both knees for a half "cross-legged seat." At the same time, your arms make a hold-ball gesture in front of left chest, left hand above the right. Then draw right foot to the inside of left foot, toes on floor. Look at left forearm. (Figs 4-1-139, 4-1-140, 4-1-141)

2) Turn body to the right as right foot takes a step forward to the right for a right bow stance. At the same time, raise right hand to the front of right temple, palm obliquely upward, while left palm moves in a small leftward-downward arc before pushing it out forward and upward to nose level. Look at left hand. (Figs 4-1-142, 4-1-143, 4-1-144)

3) Turn body slightly to the right (5 o'clock), shifting weight slightly backward, with toes of right foot turning a bit outward. Then shift weight back onto right leg and draw left foot to the inside of right foot, toes on floor.

Meanwhile, your arms make a hold-ball gesture in front of right part of chest, right hand above the left. Look at right forearm. (Figs 4-1-145, 4-1-146)

4) Repeat movements in 2), reversing "right" and "left" . (Figs 4-1-147, 4-1-148, 4-1-149)

Key points: Do not lean forward or

Fig 4-1-139

Fig 4-1-140

Fig 4-1-141

Fig 4-1-142

Fig 4-1-143

Fig 4-1-144

Fig 4-1-145

Fig 4-1-146

Fig 4-1-147

Fig 4-1-148

Fig 4-1-149

raise shoulders when pushing hands forward. Movements of hands should be coordinated with those of waist and legs. Keep a transverse distance of about 30 cm between heels in bow stance. Face 2 o'clock in final position.

Form 19 Hai-Di-Zhen: Thrusting the Hand Downward

Draw right foot half a step forward, shift weight onto right leg and move left foot a bit forward, toes on floor for a left empty stance. At the same time, body turning slightly to the right (4 o'clock), right hand moves down in front of body, then up to around the ear level on the right. Body turning slightly to the left (3 o'clock), right hand reaches down, fingers pointing downward with palm facing left, until it is below the waist while left hand moves down and forward in an arc until it comes to stop at about waist height over the left leg, palm down. Look at floor ahead. (Figs 4-1-150, 4-1-151)

Fig 4-1-150

Fig 4-1-151

Key points: Do not lean too much forward. Keep head erect and buttocks in. Left leg bends slightly. Face 3 o'clock in final position.

Form 20 Shan-Tong-Bi: Unfurling Arms like a Fan

Turn body slightly to the right (4 o'clock), and take a step forward with left foot forming a left bow stance. At the same time, raise right hand with elbow bending, finishing above right temple level, palm turning obliquely upward with thumb pointing down, while left palm moves a bit upward and then pushes forward at nose level. Look at left hand. (Figs 4-1-152, 4-1-153, 4-1-154)

Key points: Keep torso erect and waist and hips relaxed. Do not straighten arm when you push left palm forward. Palm movements should be synchronized with the taking of bow stance, with your back muscles stretching. Keep a transverse distance of less than 10 cm between heels. Face 3 o'clock in final position.

Fig 4-1-152   Fig 4-1-153   Fig 4-1-154

Form 21 Zhuan Shen Ban Lan Chui: Deflecting, Parrying and Punching

1) Sit back and shift weight onto right leg. Turn body to the right (6 o'clock), with toes of left foot turning inward. Then shift weight again onto left leg. Simultaneously, right hand moves with body turning, in a right-ward-downward arc, formed into fist, held about the level of left ribs with the palm down, while left hand moves up to the front of forehead, with palm turned obliquely upward. Look straight ahead. (Figs 4-1-155, 4-1-156a, 4-1-156b)

2) Turn body to the right (8 o'clock), bringing right fist up and then forward and downward for a backhand punch, while left hand lowers to the side of left hip with palm turning down. At the same time, right foot draws towards left foot and, without stopping or touching floor, takes a step forward, toes turn outward. Look at right fist.

(Figs 4-1-157a, 4-1-157b, 4-1-158)

3) Shift weight onto right leg and take a step forward with left foot. At the same time, parry with left hand by moving it sideways and up to the front, palm turning slightly downward while right fist withdraws to the side of right hip with forearm rotating internally and then externally, so that the fist is turned down and then up again. Look at left hand. (Figs 4-1-159, 4-1-160)

4) Bend left leg for a left bow stance and punch with right fist at chest level, with palm leftward, while left hand withdraws to the inside of right forearm. Look at right fist. (Fig 4-1-161)

Key points: Clench right fist loosely. In the process that right fist retreats, the forearm rotates inward in an arc, and then rotates outward, finishing by the side of right waist with the fist facing up, Keep shoulders and elbows lowered and right arm slightly bent. Face 9 o'clock in final position.

Fig 4-1-155

Fig 4-1-156a

Fig 4-1-156b

Fig 4-1-157a

Fig 4-1-157b

Fig 4-1-158

Fig 4-1-159

Fig 4-1-160

Fig 4-1-161

CHINESE PHYSICAL EXERCISES AND HEALTH CARE

Form 22 Ru Feng Si Bi: Apparent Sealing and Closing

l) Move left hand forward and under right wrist, simultaneously opening right fist. Separate hands and pull them back slowly, palms up, at the same time, sit back with toes of left foot rising and weight shifting onto right leg. Look straight ahead. (Figs 4-1-162, 4-1-163, 4-1-164)

2) Turn palms down in front of chest. Pull both hands back to the front of

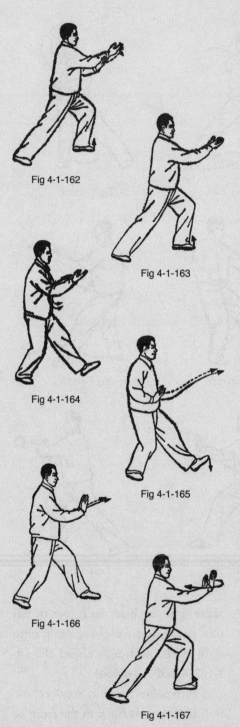

Fig 4-1-162

Fig 4-1-163

Fig 4-1-164

Fig 4-1-165

Fig 4-1-166

Fig 4-1-167

abdomen and then push them forward and upward until wrists are at shoulder level, palms facing forward. At the same time, Bend left leg for a left bow stance. Look straight ahead. (Figs 4-1-165, 4-1-166, 4-1-167)

Key points: Do not lean backward or protrude buttocks when sitting back. Do not pull arms back straight. Relax your shoulders and turn elbows a bit outward. Hands should be no farther than shoulder-width apart when you push them forward. Face 9 o'clock in final position.

Form 23 Shi-Zi-Shou: Crossing Hands

1) Bend right knee, sit back and shift weight onto right leg, which bends at knee. Turn body to the right (1 o'clock) with toes of left foot turning inward. Following the turning of body, move both hands sideways in a horizontal arc at shoulder level, palms facing forward and elbows slightly bending. Meanwhile, turn toes of right foot slightly outward and shift weight onto right leg. Look at right hand. (Figs 4-1-168, 4-1-169)

2) Shift weight slowly onto left leg with toes of right foot turning inward. Then bring right foot towards left foot so that they are parallel to each other and shoulder-width apart; straighten legs gradually. At the same time, move

Fig 4-1-168

Fig 4-1-169

Fig 4-1-170

Fig 4-1-171

when separating or crossing hands. Keep body and head erect with chin tucking slightly inward. Keep arms rounded in a comfortable position, with shoulders and elbows held down. Face 12 o'clock in final position.

Form 24 Closing Form

Turn palms hands forward and downward while lowering both hands gradually to the side of hips. Look straight ahead. (Figs 4-1-172, 4-1-173, 4-1-174)

Key points: Keep whole body relaxed and draw a deep breath (exhalation to be somewhat prolonged) when you lower hands. Bring left foot close to right foot after your breath is even. Walk about for complete recovery.

Fig 4-1-172

Fig 4-1-174

Fig 4-1-173

both hands down in a vertical arc to cross them at wrist first in front of abdomen and then in front of chest, left hand is nearer to body and both palms facing inward. Look straight ahead. (Figs 4-1-170, 4-1-171)

Key points: Do not lean forward

Taiji swordplay is one set of the *Taiji* exercises, which one performs with the sword, which may be made of metal, wood or bamboo, of such a length that its tip is higher than your ear but lower than the top of your head when you hold it in the preparatory position.

Like barehanded *Taiji* exercises, this swordplay is guided by the following principles:

1) All movements should be guided by consciousness (mind-intention). Concentrate your thoughts on every movement you perform. Do not look around or let your mind wander when doing the exercises.

2) All movements should be circular, relaxed and soft, but not loose and inert. They should follow one another in a continuous flow without apparent pauses—just like "a flowing stream or a flying cloud," or "silk being drawn out from a cocoon."

3) All movements of the head, body, arms, legs and eyes should be well coordinated. Use your torso to lead your limbs, with your waist acting as the hinges. Do not let your body rise and fall abruptly. Movements of the body should be synchronized with those of the sword. Breathing should be deep and even, and in harmony with your movements.

4) Move at an even and slow pace. The whole set takes about three minutes.

5) The amount of exercise for each session may be determined by your health condition and the length of time you can afford. You may do the whole set once or several times, you may practice only one or several sections, or one or several forms.

Ways to Hold the Sword

1. Sword in left hand

When you are carrying the sword with your left hand, place thumb on one side, middle finger and ring finger on the other side of the guard with index finger straightened and rested on the handle. Carry the sword vertical to the ground with the tip of the sword facing upwards and the sword is hidden behind your left arm. (Fig 4-2-1)

Fig 4-2-1

2. Sword in right hand

When you are practicing with the sword in the right hand, place the

Fig 4-2-2

Fig 4-2-4

middle finger and the ring finger on one side and thumb on the other side of the handle. Hold the handle as close to the wrist guard as possible with these fingers, and use mainly these three fingers to hold the sword. The index and the little fingers should be resting beside them, stretched but relaxed, tightened or moved on when needed. The index finger and the thumb are often rested on the guard. The palm should be hollow for flexibility in the sense that the palm should not be tightly against the handle of the sword. (Fig 4-2-2)

3. Sword-fingers

Hold the empty hand in a sword-finger gesture (the index and middle fingers stretching out, and other fingers curved with the thumb on the top touching the nails). (Fig 4-2-3)

Fig 4-2-3

Preparatory Position

Stand upright with feet shoulder-width apart, toes pointing forward, arms hanging naturally at sides. Look straight ahead and keep shoulders down. Hold sword in left hand, blade

touching arm and pointing up, forefinger resting on handle while thumb and other fingers all curl around and hold the sword on the hilt, grasping either side of hand-guard. (Fig4-2-4)

Notes:

1) Directions are given in terms of the hours of the clock.

Begin by facing 12 o'clock, with 6 o'clock behind you, 9 o'clock at your left and 3 o'clock at your right. Thus a turn to 1 o'clock is one of 30° to the right, and a turn to 10-11 o'clock is one of 45° to the left.

2) In the illustrations, the path of the next movement is indicated by an arrow, with a solid line for the right hand and foot and a dotted one for the left hand and foot. Such lines also apply to the sword when held in right or left hand.

Commencing Form

1) Raise arms slowly to shoulder

level and turn right hand into "sword-fingers," with index and middle fingers extended, little and ring fingers bent, both nails under thumb, and both palms facing downward. Look straight ahead. (Fig 4-2-5)

Key Points: Raise arms effortlessly, with hands spaced no wider than shoulders. Do not point sword downward.

2) Turn upper torso to the right (1–2 o'clock) and shift body weight onto right leg. Bend right legs and turn torso to the left (9 o'clock) as you take a step in the same direction with left foot to form a left bow stance, right leg straightened and left leg bent at knee. At the same time, move left hand downward to the side of left hip in a curve with sword pointing up behind left arm, while right hand moves up with palm supinated and elbow bent and then with palm pronated, past right ear and forward at eye level, sword-fingers pointing forward. Look

to the right and then at fingers. (Figs 4-2-6, 4-2-7)

Key Points: While moving left arm, turn torso slightly to the right to shift weight onto right leg and then lift left foot for the bow stance. The movements of turning the torso, taking bow stance and moving arms should be even and well-coordinated.

3) Bend left elbow and extend left hand, palm down, over right hand. Supinate right palm and lower and extend arm sideways as you turn torso to the right (12 o'clock). At the same time, cross right leg in front of left leg, with both knees bent to form a half-squat sitting position, toes of right foot turned outward and left heel off floor. Look at sword-fingers. (Fig 4-2-8)

Key Points: Cross hands in front of chest before separating them. Coordinate swing of right arm with body turn.

4) Take a step forward with left foot to form a left bow stance as you turn

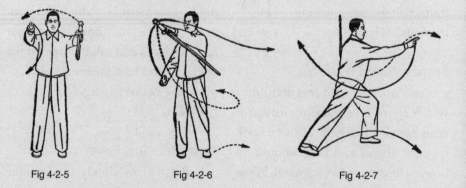

Fig 4-2-5   Fig 4-2-6   Fig 4-2-7

Fig 4-2-8

Fig 4-2-9

vertical semicircle at left side and point its tip slightly downward with a jerk. Keep right arm straight and place left hand on right wrist, in the form of sword-fingers. At the same time, bring right foot to join left foot, toes pointing forward and legs slightly bent at knee. Look at sword-tip. (Fig 4-2-10)

Key Points: Use wrist to circle sword without raising arms. Concentrate force in sword-tip when pointing sword downward. Keep torso upright and shoulders down.

Fig 4-2-10

torso to the left (9 o'clock). Move sword-fingers overhead to sword-handle, ready to take it over. Look straight ahead. (Fig 4-2-9)

Key Points: Lift left foot and turn head to the left before moving right arm. Keep torso and shoulders relaxed. Arms should not be rigid. Face 9 o'clock in final position.

Form 1 Pointing Sword with Feet Together

Move index finger of left hand towards middle finger and open right hand to take over sword-handle with tennis grip. Move sword in a clockwise

Form 2 Standing on One Leg and Thrusting

1) Take a step towards (1-2 o'clock) with right foot as you turn torso in the same direction and then place left foot beside right foot, toes on floor. At the same time, move right hand downward and rightward so that sword-tip describes a vertical semicircle through wrist action until it stops above right shoulder. Sword-fingers follow right hand and stop in front of right

Fig 4-2-11

Fig 4-2-12

Fig 4-2-13

downward. At the same time, raise right hand slowly to thrust sword overhead towards 9 o'clock, with thumb side down and force concentrated in sword-tip, which is a little lower than handle. Simultaneously with body turn, move sword-fingers past chin and point them forward at eye level. Look at sword-fingers. (Fig 4-2-13)

Key Points: Do not pause in the middle of movements. Stand firm without leaning forward or backward.

Form 3 Sweeping Sword in Crouch

1) Turn torso to the right (1-2 o'clock) and cut in the same direction until sword-blade is in a horizontal line with right arm, which is extended in front of body, with sword-fingers resting on wrist. With body turn, bend right knee and extend left foot down towards 7-8 o'clock to form a right bow stance. Look at sword-tip. (Fig 4-2-14)

2) Turn torso to the left (9 o'clock) and move sword-fingers in an arc going down, left, up and then to the front of left temple, palm facing obliquely upward. At the same time, supinate right hand and sweep sword downward to upper left with force concentrated in its middle part. Simultaneously with body turn, bend right

shoulder. Look at sword-tip. (Figs 4-2-11, 4-2-12)

2) Turn torso to the left (10-11 o'clock) and lift left knee to stand on one leg, toes of left foot pointing

Fig 4-2-14

Fig 4-2-15

knee and stretch out left leg to form a half crouch; then rise up and shift weight onto left leg for a left bow stance, with toes of right foot turned inward and those of left foot turned outward. Look at sword-tip. (Fig 4-2-15)

Key Points: Movements should be continuous. Keep torso upright while taking a bow stance. Face 9 o'clock in final position.

Form 4 Carry Sword to the Right

Take a step towards 10-11 o'clock with right foot past the inside of left foot for a right bow stance. At the same time, carry sword forward and, with right hand pronated, withdraw it slowly to the right, with right arm bent at elbow in front of right ribs, sword-tip raised a little above handle, sword-fingers resting on right wrist and force concentrated on right edge of sword-blade. Look at sword-tip. (Fig 4-2-16)

Key Points: Withdraw sword and

bend knee simultaneously.

Fig 4-2-16

Form 5 Carry Sword to the Left

Carry sword forward and then, with right hand supinated, withdraw it slowly until arm is bent at elbow in front of left ribs, with force concentrated on left edge of sword-blade. At the same time, move sword-fingers in a downward-leftward-upward curve to the front of left temple, palm facing obliquely upward, while left foot takes a step towards 7-8 o'clock past the inside of right foot for a left bow stance. Look at sword-tip. (Fig 4-2-17)

Key Points: See Form 4.

Fig 4-2-17

Fig 4-2-18

Form 6 Stand on One Leg and Cut with Armswing

Place right foot beside left foot, toes on floor, while left hand dropping on right wrist. Turn torso to the left (6 o'clock) as you move sword downward past left side of body and then, with a turnover of wrist in a left-upward curve to cut down in front of body, with force concentrated on lower edge of sword-blade. At the same time, swing sword-fingers in a downward, backward and upward curve to the front of left temple, with palm facing obliquely upward. While circling sword clockwise, take a step forward with right foot and lift left knee to stand on one leg. Look at sword-tip. (Figs 4-2-18, 4-2-19, 4-2-20)

Key Points: In circling sword, turn torso and head to the left and then back to face 9 o'clock in final position. Coordinate knee-lifting with cutting action. All movements should be continuous.

Fig 4-2-19

Fig 4-2-20

Form 7 Step Back and Withdraw Sword

Set left foot on floor one step behind right foot, with left leg bent at knee, as torso turns slightly to 8 o'clock. Take half a step backward with right foot, toes on floor for a right empty stance. At the same time, withdraw sword until its handle comes close to left ribs, palm facing inward and sword-tip pointing slightly upward, while sword-fingers drop on right wrist. Look at sword-tip. (Fig 4-2-21)

Key Points: Draw right foot and sword back simultaneously. Keep torso upright.

Form 8 Stand on One Leg and Thrust

Turn torso slightly to the right (9 o'clock). Take a step forward with right foot and lift left knee to stand on one leg. At the same time, thrust sword forward and upward, right palm up, with force concentrated on sword-tip. (Fig 4-2-22)

Key Points: Lean slightly forward without thrusting out chest. Stand firmly on one leg. Face 9 o'clock in final position.

Form 9 Plunge Sword Downward in Empty Stance

Set left foot one step back on floor and move right foot a bit backward, toes on floor for a right empty stance. At the same time, with body turning slightly to the left (8 o'clock) and then to the right (10-11 o'clock), move sword in a leftward, downward and rightward curve until sword-tip points obliquely downward at knee level at right side of body, force concentrated on lower edge of blade, while sword-fingers move in a downward-backward-upward curve to the front of left temple, palm facing obliquely upward. Look ahead to the right. (Fig 4-2-23)

Fig 4-2-21

Fig 4-2-22

Fig 4-2-23

CHINESE PHYSICAL EXERCISES AND HEALTH CARE

Key Points: The movements of taking empty stance and plunging sword downward should be well coordinated. Face 10 o'clock in final position.

Form 10 Thrust in Left Bow Stance

Take a step backward to the right with right foot and move left foot close to right foot and then take a step towards 8 o'clock for a left bow stance. At the same time, with body turning slightly to the right (12 o'clock) and then to the left (9 o'clock), bring sword upward and then downward and forward in a thrust, palm up, with force concentrated on sword-tip, while sword-fingers move in a rightward-downward-leftward-upward curve to the front of left temple, arm rounded and palm facing obliquely upward. Look at sword-tip. (Figs 4-2-24, 4-2-25)

Key Points: Rotate right arm internally and then externally while drawing sword back and then thrust sword

forward from right waist. Sword-fingers should touch right wrist before circling up. Face 9 o'clock in final position.

Form 11 Turn Round and Carry Sword

1) Shift weight onto right leg and turn toes of left foot inward. Turn torso to the right (12 o'clock) and shift weight onto left leg again. Lift right foot to the inside of lower left leg. At the same time, draw sword back to place it horizontal in front of chest, palm down, while sword-fingers rest on right wrist. Look to the left. (Fig 4-2-26)

2) Turn torso further to the right (3 o'clock) as right foot takes a step towards 4-5 o'clock for a right bow stance. At the same time, with palm pronated, carry sword to the right, force concentrated on outer edge of blade, sword-tip above eye level and sword-fingers still on right wrist. Look

Fig 4-2-24

Fig 4-2-25

Fig 4-2-26

Fig 4-2-27

Fig 4-2-28

of blade and sword-tip at eye level. Move sword-fingers in a downward, leftward and upward curve and return them to right wrist. Look at sword-tip. (Fig 4-2-28)

Key Points: Do not protrude buttocks when carrying sword backward. Torso faces 1 o'clock in final position.

at sword-tip. (Fig 4-2-27)

Key Points: Weight transfer and formation of bow step should be coordinated with body turn. Face 3 o'clock in final position.

Form 12 Retreat and Carry Sword

Lift left foot and set it down on the same spot after describing a small circle. Shift weight onto left leg and draw right foot back to the inside of left foot, toes on floor. At the same time, turn torso slightly to the left (1 o'clock) and, with right hand supinated, carry sword to the left, with force concentrated on outer edge

Form 13 Lift Knee and Hold Sword with Both Hands

1) Take a step backward with right foot and a small one with left foot, toes on floor. At the same time, part hands to the sides, palms down and sword-tip in front of chest. (Fig 4-2-29)

2) Move left foot a bit forward and lift right knee to stand on one leg. At the same time, hold right hand with left hand, arms slightly bent and sword pointing forward, sword-tip at neck level. Look straight ahead. (Fig 4-2-30)

Key Points: Keep the supporting left leg straight, toes of right foot pointing naturally downward. Hold torso erect.

Fig 4-2-29

concentrated on sword-tip, while sword-fingers move in a backward-upward curve to the front of left temple, palm facing obliquely upward. Look at sword-tip. (Fig 4-2-33)

Key Points: Coordinate steps with

Fig 4-2-30

Fig 4-2-31

Form 14 Hop and Thrust

1) Set right foot on floor in front of left foot and shift weight forward. With a push against toes of right foot, take a step forward with left foot. Just before left foot touches floor, raise right foot to the inside of left lower leg. At the same time, draw sword a bit backward and thrust it forward as you set right foot on floor. Then, as left foot lands on floor, part hands to both sides, with left hand turned into sword-fingers and both palms facing downward. Look straight ahead. (Figs 4-2-31, 4-2-32)

2) As right foot takes a step forward for a right bow stance, thrust sword forward with palm supinated and force

Fig 4-2-32

Fig 4-2-33

hand movements. Keep sword level and steady after thrust. Torso faces 1-2 o'clock in final position.

Form 15 Swing Up Sword in Left Empty Stance

Shift weight onto left leg and turn torso to the left (10-11 o'clock) as your right foot draws back, and takes a small step forward with toes turned outward. Then turn torso to the right (3 o'clock) and shift weight onto right leg as you take a step forward with left foot, toes on floor for a left empty stance. Simultaneously with body turns, move sword in a vertical circle until sword-handle stops in front of right temple, with force concentrated on front part of blade, sword-tip pointing slightly downward at mouth level and right palm facing outward. When body turns to the left, drop sword-fingers to left ribs to join right wrist£Æ Look straight ahead. (Figs 4-2-34, 4-2-35)

Key Points: Move sword in a full circle. Face 3 o'clock in final position.

Form 16 Swing Up Sword in Right Bow Stance

Turn torso to the right (6 o'clock) as you move up sword to right side, palm facing for-ward while sword-fingers follow right forearm. Then turn torso to the left (1-2 o'clock) as you take a

Fig 4-2-34

Fig 4-2-35

small step forward with left foot and a big one with right foot for a right bow stance. At the same time, swing up sword until it comes to shoulder level, sword-tip pointing slightly downward, force concentrated on front part of blade and palm facing rightward, while sword-fingers are placed above left temple, palm facing obliquely upward. Look straight ahead. (Figs 4-2-36, 4-2-37)

Key Points: When sword circles backward, turn torso backward and follow sword-tip with eyes. All movements should be continuous. Torso faces 1-2 o'clock in final position.

Fig 4-2-36

Fig 4-2-37

2) With torso turning slightly to the right (11 o'clock), shift weight onto right leg, slightly bent at knee; draw left foot back, toes on floor for a left empty stance. At the same time, draw sword back to right side with sword-tip pointing slightly downward, while sword-fingers move back to chest and then past chin to the front at eye level. Look at sword-fingers. (Fig 4-2-40)

Fig 4-2-38

Fig 4-2-39

Fig 4-2-40

Form 17 Turn Round and Withdraw Sword

1) Turn torso to the left (12 o'clock) and shift weight onto left leg to form a side bow stance with right leg straightened, toes turned inward, left leg bent at knee and toes turned a bit outward. At the same time, draw sword-handle to the front of chest with blade leveled and sword-tip pointing a little backward to the right, while sword-fingers drop on right wrist. Then turn torso further to the left (10 o'clock) and cut in the same direction until sword blade is leveled, force concentrated on lower edge, sword-fingers remaining on right wrist. Look at sword-tip. (Figs 4-2-38, 4-2-39)

Key Points: Maintain harmony in the whole movement. Face 10 o'clock in final position.

Form 18 Thrust with Feet Together

Take a small sidestep with left foot and move right foot to join it. Stand upright and face 9 o'clock. At the same time, move left hand in a downward curve to hold right hand from under and thrust sword forward at chest level, both palms up and force concentrated on sword-tip. Look straight ahead. (Fig 4-2-41)

Key Points: Join feet and thrust sword at the same time. Keep arms slightly bent and stand upright without protruding chest. Face 9 o'clock in final position.

Form 19 Parry in Left Bow Stance

Pronate right hand and draw sword back. Move sword in a rightward and backward curve as you turn torso to the right (10-11 o'clock) and then continuously in a downward-forward parry as you turn torso to the left (7-8 o'clock), palm facing obliquely inward, sword-blade at head level and force concentrated on upper edge. At the same time, move sword-fingers in a downward-upward curve to the left above temple, palm facing obliquely

upward. Simultaneously with body turn to 7-8 o'clock, take a step in the same direction with left foot and bend left leg for a left bow stance. Eyes follow sword and look straight ahead in final position. (Figs 4-2-42, 4-2-43)

Fig 4-2-41

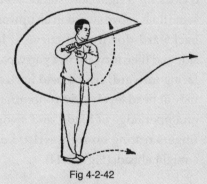

Fig 4-2-42

Fig 4-2-43

Key Points: Turn body with the circling sword, first to the right and then to the left. Bend right leg slightly before left foot steps forward. Move sword-fingers together with right hand until they separate at upper right. Face 7-8 o'clock in final position.

Form 20 Parry in Right Bow Stance

Shift weight a bit backward and turn toes of left foot outward. Turn torso to the left (6 o'clock) and then to the right (9 o'clock) as right foot takes a step past inside of left foot towards 10-11 o'clock for a right bow stance. At the same time, move sword in an upward-backward-downward curve at left side and then forward in a parry, palm facing forward, sword held horizontally at head level, force concentrated on upper edge of blade, and sword-fingers resting on right wrist. Look straight ahead. (Fig 4-2-44)

Key Points: Move sword in a big circle. Eyes follow sword. Face 9 o'clock in final position.

Form 21 Parry in Left Bow Stance

Shift weight a bit backward and turn toes of right foot outward. Turn torso to the right (10-11 o'clock) and then to the left (7-8 o'clock) as left foot takes a step past inside of right foot towards 7-8 o'clock for a left bow stance. At the same time, move sword in an upward-backward-downward curve at right side and then forward in a parry, palm facing obliquely upward, sword held horizontally at head level and force concentrated on upper edge of blade. At the same time move sword-fingers in a downward-rightward-upward circle to the left above left temple, palm facing obliquely upward. (Fig 4-2-45)

Key Points: Same as those for Form 20.

Fig 4-2-44

Fig 4-2-45

Form 22 Step Forward and Plunge Backward

1) Turn torso to the right (12 o'clock) as right foot takes a step to cross left leg in front, toes turned outward and left heel off floor. At the same time, lower sword-tip while sword-fingers drop on right wrist. Then plunge sword to the right while sword-fingers point to the left. Stretch arms sideways, with left palm facing downward and right palm facing forward. Look at sword-tip. (Fig 4-2-46)

2) Turn torso to the left (9 o'clock) as left foot takes a step forward for a left bow stance. At the same time, bend right elbow to bring sword-tip up to the front in a thrust, palm facing outward, sword-fingers resting on right wrist and force concentrated on sword-tip, which is lower than handle. Look at sword-tip. (Fig 4-2-47)

Key Points: Movements should be continuous. Do not lean too much forward when thrusting sword forward. Face 9 o'clock in final position.

Form 23 Turn Round to Cut

With toes of left foot turned inward, shift weight onto right leg and then back onto left leg. Turn about on the right (3 o'clock) and move right foot backward and then towards 4 o'clock for a right bow stance. At the same time, cut in the same direction, with force concentrated on lower edge of blade, while sword-fingers move in a downward-upward curve to the left above left temple, palm facing obliquely upward. Look at sword-tip. (Fig 4-2-48)

Fig 4-2-46

Fig 4-2-47

Fig 4-2-48

Key Points: Coordinate the cutting movement with body turn and the taking of bow stance. Torso faces 2 o'clock in final position.

Form 24 Point Sword in Right Empty Stance

Lift left foot and turn torso to the left (1 o'clock). Set left foot on floor towards 12 o'clock, toes turned outward. Place right foot in front of left foot, toes on floor for a right empty stance. Simultaneously with body turn, move up sword and point it obliquely downward, with right arm stretched forward and force concentrated on sword-tip, while sword-fingers drop in a circle on left side to rest on right wrist. Look at sword-tip. (Fig 4-2-49)

Key Points: Point sword downward through wrist action. Coordinate this movement with the landing of right foot. Keep body upright.

Form 25 Stand on One Leg and Hold Sword Level

Place right foot behind left foot. Pivoting on balls of both feet, turn body to the right (3 o'clock). Lift left knee to stand on one leg. At the same time, move sword in a leftward-downward-upward curve and, with the body turn, raise sword a bit above head, blade leveled and force concentrated on its upper edge and sword-fingers

resting on right wrist. Look straight ahead. (Fig 4-2-50)

Key Points: Set right foot down on ball first. Lift left knee and raise sword simultaneously. Stand firmly with right leg naturally straightened. Face 3 o' clock in final position.

Fig 4-2-49

Fig 4-2-50

Form 26 Cut in Bow Stance

1) Set left foot on floor in front of right foot with toes pointing leftward and turn body to left (11 o'clock) to form a half "cross-legged seat," right heel off floor. At the same time, move sword downward to left side, tip pointing leftward and sword-fingers

Fig 4-2-51

Fig 4-2-52

resting on right wrist. Look at sword-tip. (Fig 4-2-51)

2) Take a step towards 3 o'clock with right foot for a right bow stance as you turn body to the right (2 o'clock). At the same time, with a turn of right wrist, raise sword and cut to the front, blade leveled, force concentrated on lower edge and palm facing obliquely upward, while sword-fingers move to the left above left temple. Look at sword-tip. (Fig 4-2-52)

Key Points: Turn body to the left and then to the right. Eyes follow sword-tip. Torso faces 2 o'clock in final position.

Form 27 Cut with Armswing in Empty Stance

1) Shift weight slightly backward and turn body to the right (6 o'clock) to form a cross step, toes of right foot turned outward and left the heel off the floor. At the same time, swing sword downward to right side at shoulder level, palm facing backward, while sword-fingers move to the front of right shoulder. Look at sword-tip. (Fig 4-2-53)

2) Turn body to the left (2 o'clock) as you take a small step forward with left foot, toes turned outward. Then take a step forward with right foot, toes on floor for a right empty stance. At the same time, with an outward rotation of right arm, raise sword and cut until sword-tip drops to knee level, force concentrated on lower edge of blade, while sword-fingers move downward past abdomen and stop inside right forearm. Look at sword-tip. (Fig 4-2-54)

Key Points: Movements should be continuous. Torso faces 2 o'clock in final position.

Form 28 Step Back to Strike

Turn torso to the right (6 o'clock) as

right foot takes a big step backward and left heel turns outward and left leg straightens into a right-side bow stance. At the same time, swing sword to right side, palm facing obliquely upward, sword-tip above head level and force concentrated on front part

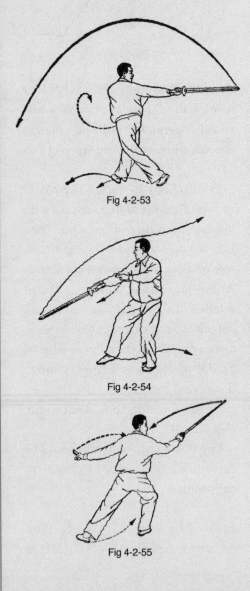

Fig 4-2-53

Fig 4-2-54

Fig 4-2-55

of blade, while left arm is extended sideways, sword-fingers a little lower than shoulder level and palm down. Look at sword-tip. (Fig 4-2-55)

Key points: Part hands and turn body simultaneously. Step back and strike towards 7-8 o'clock.

Form 29　Step Forward to Thrust

1) Turn body slightly to the right (7-8 o'clock), lift left foot and place it beside right lower leg. At the same time, pronate right palm to level sword across right part of chest, tip pointing a bit forward to the left, while sword-fingers move up in a curve in front of the right shoulder. Look straight ahead. (Fig 4-2-57)

2) Turn torso towards 1-2 o'clock as left foot takes a small step in the same direction, toes turned outward, and right foot takes a big step towards 3 o'clock for a right bow stance. Following body turn, thrust sword forward with force concentrated on sword-tip, palm up, while sword-fingers move in a downward-forward-upward curve to the left above left temple, palm facing obliquely upward. Look at sword-tip. (Fig 4-2-57)

Key Points: Turn body after left foot has been brought up close to right lower leg. Step forward with right foot when left foot is firm on floor. The

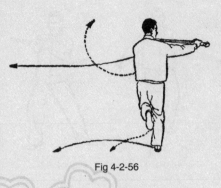

Fig 4-2-56

Fig 4-2-57

movements of torso and hands should be coordinated with those of legs. Torso faces 1-2 o'clock in final position.

Form 30 Withdraw Sword in T-Step

Shift weight backward and withdraw right foot to the inside of left foot, toes on floor to form a right " T-step." At the same time, bend right elbow to draw sword-handle to left ribs, sword-tip pointing up to the right and palm facing inward, while sword-fingers drop on handle. Look at sword-tip. (Fig 4-2-58)

Fig 4-2-58

Key Points: Withdraw sword and right foot simultaneously. Torso should be kept erect and face 12 o'clock in final position.

Form 31 Circle Sword Horizontally

1) Turn torso slightly to the right (2 o'clock) and take a step forward with right foot, toes of both feet turned outward. Turn right palm downward to level sword-blade in front of chest. (Fig 4-2-59)

2) Shift weight onto right leg as you continue to turn body to the right (8 o'clock) and move left foot round right foot, their toes turned inward. Then, Using ball of left foot as pivot, continue to turn body to the right (12 o'clock), moving right foot round left foot and drawing left foot a bit backward, toes on floor for a left empty stance. Following body turn, carry sword in a horizontal circle with force concentrated on outer edge of

Fig 4-2-59   Fig 4-2-60   Fig 4-2-61   Fig 4-2-62

blade. When taking empty stance, part hands to both sides of hips, palms down, blade pointing up to the left in front of body. Look straight ahead. (Figs 4-2-60, 4-2-61)

Key Points: Turn about at an even pace with torso and head upright. Face 12 o'clock in final position.

Form 32 Thrust Forward in Bow Stance

Take half a step forward with left foot for a left bow stance. At the same time, thrust sword forward at chest level, with force concentrated on sword-tip and sword-fingers resting on right wrist. Look straight ahead. (Fig 4-2-62)

Key Points: Take a bow stance and thrust forward simultaneously.

Closing Form

1) Shift weight backward and turn torso to the right (2 o'clock). At the same time withdraw sword to right side with palm facing inward, and move left hand to hold hand-guard. Look at sword-blade. (Fig 4-2-63)

2) Turn body to the left (12 o'clock) and shift weight onto left leg. Place right foot beside left foot, so that the two feet are shoulder-width apart, toes pointing forward. At the same time, left hand takes over sword with a reverse grasp and drops to left side of body, palm facing backward and forefinger on handle, sword-blade pointing up behind arm, while right hand is turned into sword-fingers and moves in an upward, leftward and downward curve to right side of body. Keep whole body relaxed and look straight ahead. (Fig 4-2-64)

Fig 4-2-63   Fig 4-2-64

III Taiji Push-Hand Exercises

Tuishou or "push hand," is a kind of sparring exercises in *taijiquan*.

There is a great variety of hand movements in *taiji* routines, but almost all of them are done with either "receding" or "engaging" force. The former calls for "no forcible contact," which means retreating when the opponent advances so as to "neutralize" the oncoming force, while the latter admits of "no separation," which means advancing when the opponent retreats so as to pin him down. These are actually two aspects of every circular movement in *taiji* routines—aspects that are opposite and complementary to each other.

Taijiquan places "neutralizing" before "hitting" and stresses "subduing the vigorous by the soft," or countering a big force with a small one. Such characteristics find concentrated expressions in *tuishou* exercises. By doing these exercises regularly, those who have learned some forms of *taijiquan* will get a deeper understanding of the movements, and those who know nothing about *taiji* may improve their health and ability in self-defence all the same.

Students of *tuishou* are advised to bear the following points in mind:

1) Start with the basic movements before taking up exercises in fixed position. That is, starting without taking steps and then with steps.

2) Whether in an advance or a retreat, always try to "feel" the opponent's force to sound out whether it is strong or weak and whether it is "solid," or "void," so as to put him at a disadvantage.

3) Gear your hand pushes to body movements. Move your waist before taking a step when you respond to a push.

4) Keep your arms in constant contact with your opponent. Go on with the pushing movement when the two persons' hands happen to disengage due to the improper amount of force applied. You may break the force, but not the thread of your thought.

Basic Movements

1. Preparatory position

Partner A (wearing white shoes) and partner B (wearing black shoes) stand at attention, completely relaxed and facing each other, with such a distance between them that when they stretch their arms forward, their fists just touch each other. (Fig 4-3-1)

Starting position: Each turns slightly to the left and take a step forward with right foot so that the inner part of his right foot faces that of his partner's, with a distance of 10-20 cm between them. Then both stretch right arms forward, elbow slightly bent and palm facing inward, so that their right wrists cross each other in a "joining hands" position, while left hands hang naturally at left side of body and center of gravity is between legs. (Fig 4-3-2)

Points: Their right wrists that have come into contact should use neither too much nor too little force—they should use just enough force to push each other aside.

Fig 4-3-1

Fig 4-3-2

2. Push single hand

1) Partner A uses right palm to push partner B's right wrist horizontally forward; at the same time he bends right leg forward and shifts weight slightly with it, with the aim of pressing partner B's right chest with right palm. (Fig 4-3-3)

With partner A's force bearing down on him partner B draws back right palm with a force neither too strong nor too weak; at the same time he bends left leg slightly, shifts weight backward and turns torso to the right, and with right palm shoves partner A's hand away from his chest. (Fig 4-3-4)

2) Following the above movement, partner B immediately turns right palm to push partner A's wrist horizontally forward with the aim of pressing on his right chest (Fig 4-3-5). Partner A then cushions partner B's push with right hand and withdraws right arm naturally, bends left leg, shifts weight backward and turns torso to the right so that partner B's right palm will fall wide of the target (Fig 4-3-6). They practice in this way repeatedlly, pushing each other's hand in horizontal circles.

Application of force:

When partner A pushes partner B with a "pressing" force, partner B turns his waist to neutralize it. Partner A acts in the same way when partner B pushes.

While using a "pressing" force, don't lean the torso too far forward; while "neutralizing" an oncoming force, turn waist, withdraw hip to shift weight backward, but never lean backward. The arms of both persons should constantly maintain a force that is neither too weak nor too strong and should follow each other in bending or stretching, without relaxing or breaking off the force, or coming into stiff forcible contact. Their wrists are interlocked in a continuous twisting movement. Their left hands should move naturally in coordination with waist and leg movements.

3) Starting from the position shown in Fig 4-3-2, partner A uses right palm to push and press partner B's wrist forward and upward with the aim of hitting partner B's face; at the same time, he bends right leg and shifts weight slightly forward. Using a force neither too weak nor too strong, partner B cushions the oncoming force with right hand, and as a follow-up raises arm, bends left leg slightly and shifts weight a little backward, turns torso to the right to shove partner A's right palm to the right side of head so that it will fall wide of the mark. (Fig 4-3-7)

Fig 4-3-3

Fig 4-3-4

Fig 4-3-5

Fig 4-3-6

Fig 4-3-7

4) Partner B turns right palm slowly and pushes and presses it downward and forward with the aim of pressing partner A's right ribs. Partner A cushions the oncoming force with right hand, using a force neither too weak nor too strong; then he withdraws right arm and at the same time bends left leg, turns torso to the right, shifts weight backward and shoves partner B's right hand to the right side of his body so to lead it off the target. (Fig 4-3-8, 4-3-9)

5) When partner A pushes right hand towards partner B's face, partner B turns torso slightly to the right and at the same time uses right hand to shove partner A's right hand to the right side of his head with a force neither too weak nor too strong, so that partner A's hand will be led off the mark; as a follow-up, partner B pushes right hand towards partner A's face. Partner A turns torso to the right to shove partner B's right hand away, then turns palm again and moves it forward and downward to push and press partner B's right ribs. (Fig 4-3-10, 4-3-11, 4-3-12)

They can practice these movements repeatedly, pushing hands in vertical circles. They can push with right and left hands alternately, changing leg movements accordingly.

Fig 4-3-8

Fig 4-3-9

Fig 4-3-10

Fig 4-3-11

Fig 4-3-12

3. Push both hands in horizontal circles

1) After the two partners have brought their right hands into contact, each rests left palm on the other's right elbow. (Fig 4-3-13)

Partner A turns right palm outward and pushes and presses partner B's right wrist forward and downward. At the same time he pushes and presses partner B's right elbow with left hand in the same direction with the aim of forcing Partner B's right arm against his own chest to make its movement impossible. This is generally called a "pressing" force. (Figs 4-3-14, 4-3--15)

Partner B cushions partner A's "pressing" force with right arm, using a force that is neither too weak nor too strong, and draws partner A's right elbow naturally backward with left hand; partner B bends left leg slightly, shifts weight backward, with chest slightly drawn, and at the same time turns torso to the right and uses right arm to lead partner A's "pressing" force to the right so as to defeat its purpose. This is generally called a "neutralizing" force. (Fig 4-3-16)

2) Partner B rests right palm on partner A's right wrist, and at the same time presses both palms forward and downward. (Figs 4-3-17, 4-3-18)

The purpose and movements are the

Fig 4-3-13

Fig 4-3-14

Fig 4-3-15

Fig 4-3-16

Fig 4-3-17

Fig 4-3-18

same as partner A's as described in 2). When partner A neutralizes partner B's force or vice versa, their movements are the same. (refer to Figs 4-3-13, 4-3-14, 4-3-15, 4-3-16, 4-3-17, 4-3-18)

This exercise can be repeated over several times.

Push Hands in Fixed Position

1. Preparatory position: see Fig 4-3-2.

2. Movements

1) Ward off: Partner A and partner B cross their right hands, exerting a force that is neither too weak nor too strong. (Fig 4-3-19)

2) Deflect: Cushioning the force from partner B's right hand with his own, partner A draws right arm backward, rests right palm on partner B's right wrist; at the same time, he rests left hand on partner B's right elbow and, following the oncoming force from partner B, bends left leg, draws in hips, turns waist to the right and uses both hands to draw partner B's right arm so as to deflect his force to the right. (Fig 4-3-20)

3) Push: Following the direction of partner A's deflecting force, partner B slightly bends right leg, shifts weight slightly forward, and at the same time

rests left palm on the inside of right arm and uses right forearm to push forward at partner A's chest, with the aim of nullifying his deflecting force and changing its direction and at the same time rendering partner A's hand unmovable in front of his chest. (Fig 4-3-21)

4) Press: Following the direction of

Fig 4-3-19

Fig 4-3-20

Fig 4-3-21

partner B's oncoming force, partner A bends left leg, draws in chest, and turns waist to the left and draws hips in; at the same time he presses partner B's right arm downward and leftward with both hands to neutralize his pushing force. Immediately following this, partner A moves right hand to partner B's left elbow, while moving left hand up to partner B's left wrist; then he pushes and presses downward and forward with both palms. This is generally called a "pressing" force. (Fig 4-3-22)

5) Partner B again cushions partner A's pressing force with left arm, using a force that is neither too weak nor too strong; he counters partner A's left hand with the back of his own left hand, while right hand moves from below to the right to rest on partner A's left elbow. At the same time, he shifts weight backward, bends left leg and turns torso slightly to the left and uses left arm to ward off partner A's pressing force (but not to draw it directly backward), and then uses both hands to lead partner A's left arm slightly upward to the left, thereby assuming a deflecting posture. (Fig 4-3-23)

6) Following the direction of partner B's deflecting force, partner A, in order to keep his balance, moves right hand away from partner B's left elbow

to rest it on the inside of his own left elbow and, with both arms rounded, pushes forward at partner B's chest, thereby assuming a pressing posture. (Figs 4-3-24, 4-3-25)

Fig 4-3-22

Fig 4-3-23

Fig 4-3-24

Fig 4-3-25

7) Following the direction of partner A's push, partner B draws in chest, turns waist to the right and draws in hips to assume a pressing posture. (Figs 4-3-26, 4-3-27)

8) While partner B presses forward, partner A wards off the oncoming force with right arm, his left hand moving from below to rest again on partner B's right elbow and his torso turning to the right. At this point, partner A changes to a deflecting posture and partner B to a pushing posture. (Fig 4-3-28)

9) Change hands in fixed position: When partner B pushes right arm towards partner A's chest (refer to Fig 4-3-21), partner A does not employ the movement of pressing forward, but making use of partner B's pushing force, leads partner B's hand along with his own, and at the same times uses right hand to draw partner B's left elbow, turning torso slightly to the left. (Fig 4-3-29)

When partner B's left arm is deflected by partner A, he should change naturally to the movement of pushing left arm, with right leg still bent at knee. (Fig 4-3-30)

When partner A neutralizes partner B's pushing force and changes to the movement of pressing, partner B again moves left hand from below to rest on partner A's right elbow, with body sit-ting backward, to deflect partner A's right arm. Partner A then changes naturally to a pressing posture. (Fig 4-3-31)

Explanatory notes:

The law governing pushing hands in fixed position (without taking steps) is: When partner A deflects, partner B pushes; when partner B pushes, partner A presses; when partner A presses, partner B wards off and changes to deflecting movement once again.

Do not stress the use of force. What is important is to increase the range of movement of your body and arms. When you are pushed hard, you may accommodate and neutralize the oncoming force by assuming a sitting posture with legs bent at knee and the heel of front foot raised. Do not resist or brush aside your opponent's push vigorously; nor should you retreat unless you are pressed to such an extent as to be unable to neutralize the oncoming force. Even then you should not retreat so far as to be totally disengaged from the opponent.

After a period of practice, you will be able to stand firm, move with great amplitude and respond to the opponent's actions naturally and effectively. Thus a solid foundation will be laid for learning the exercises with steps.

Fig 4-3-26

Fig 4-3-27

Fig 4-3-28

Fig 4-3-29

Fig 4-3-30

Fig 4-3-31

Push Hands with Steps

1. Three steps forward and two steps backward

1) Starting from the position shown in Fig 4-3-1, partner A takes a step forward with left foot while partner B places right foot on the outside. They cross left hands, while partner A's right hand rests on the inside of his own left arm and partner B's right hand touches partner A's left elbow. Partner A uses left arm to do the pushing movement and partner B performs the pressing movement. (Fig 4-3-32)

2) Partner B takes the first step forward with right foot and places it by the inside of partner A's left foot. Partner A uses right hand to take on partner B's right hand above his own left forearm and rests left hand on partner B's right elbow. At the same time partner B presses partner A's right arm with both hands. (Fig 4-3-33)

3) Partner A moves left foot to take the second step backward while partner B, following partner A's retreating step, takes the second step forward with left foot and places it by the outside of partner A's right foot, ready to change to a pushing posture. (Fig 4-3-34)

4) Partner A takes the second step backward with right foot and at the same time leads partner B's right arm

to the right with both hands and turns body to assume a deflecting posture. Following partner A's deflecting movement, partner B takes the third step forward with right foot and places it by the inside of partner A's left foot, with right leg bent at knee and both arms pushing onward. Partner A slightly bends right leg, shifts weight backward and draws in hips to assume a pressing posture. (Figs 4-3-35, 4-3-36)

5) Taking advantage of partner B's pushing movement, partner A turns waist slightly to the left; at the same time he takes his first step forward by lifting left foot and placing it by the inside of partner B's right foot, while pressing forward with both hands. (Fig 4-3-37)

6) Partner B withdraws right foot quickly to take the first step backward and at the same time pulls down right hand to hold partner A's left elbow and deflect it backward. Following partner B's deflecting movement, partner A takes the second step forward with right foot and places it by the outside of partner B's left foot. (Fig 4-3-38)

7) While deflecting partner A's left arm, partner B withdraws left foot to take the second step backward. Partner A once again moves left foot to take the third step forward and places it by the inside of partner B's right foot. Then partner A once again turns to

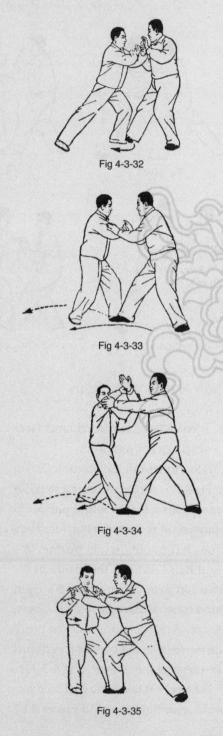

Fig 4-3-32

Fig 4-3-33

Fig 4-3-34

Fig 4-3-35

Fig 4-3-36

Fig 4-3-37

Fig 4-3-38

Fig 4-3-39

pushing movement and partner B to pressing movement, resuming the position as in Fig 4-3-32. (Fig 4-3-39)

This exercise requires the advancing side to change from pressing to pushing movement and the retreating side from warding off to deflecting movement. While advancing or retreating, both sides should use a force that is neither too weak nor too strong and should stick to each other without being separated and repeat the movements over and over again.

2. Three steps forward and three steps backward

1) Both sides start from the position in Fig 4-3-19, with right foot in front. Partner A first pushes towards partner B's chest with left arm, with right hand resting on the inside of left elbow to reinforce the pushing movement, and with right leg bent at knee. Partner B draws in hips and chest and does a pressing movement; at the same time he lifts right foot slightly and places it in front as the first step forward. In the mean time partner A lifts left foot to take the first step backward. Then partner B takes the second step forward with left foot and partner A takes the second step backward with right foot, their arm movements being the same as those shown in Figs 4-3-32~35. Following this, part-

ner B takes the third step forward with right foot and partner A takes the third step backward with left foot. The whole process is: Partner A changes from pushing to warding off and deflecting and assumes a pressing posture, while partner B changes from pressing to pushing movement. (Figs 4-3-40, 4-3-41, 4-3-42, 4-3-43, 4-3--44)

2) Partner A takes three steps forward, starting with right foot, while partner B takes three steps backward, starting with left foot. Partner A changes from pressing to pushing movement, and partner B from warding off to deflecting and pressing movement. (Figs 4-3-45, 4-3-46, 4-3-47, 4-3-48)

Fig 4-3-40

Fig 4-3-41

Fig 4-3-42

Fig 4-3-43

Fig 4-3-44

Fig 4-3-45

Fig 4-3-46

Fig 4-3-47

Fig 4-3-48

3. Big deflecting movements with moving steps

The starting position is the same as the first exercise for basic movements, with right hands crossed. (Fig 4-3-49)

Movements:

1) Partner A turns right hand outward to hold partner B's right wrist loosely, while left wrist rests on partner B's right elbow. At the same time he turns left heel outward and moves right foot half a step backward to the side of left foot, turning torsos slightly to the right to do a deflecting movement, shifting weight slightly forward. (Fig 4-3-50)

The exercise may also be done with partner A executing the deflecting movement and partner B moving right foot half a step forward

2) Partner A follows up by turning body further to the right and moving right foot a step backward to the right with both legs bent at knee while continuing with the deflecting movement, so as to force partner B to move his left foot a big step forward and lean his body forward in order to maintain his balance. (Fig 4-3-51)

3) Following partner A's deflecting movement, partner B takes another step forward with right foot and places it by the inside of partner A's left foot, shifting weight slightly onto right leg; at the same time he rests left hand on the inner side of right arm and leans towards partner A's chest with the force of the right shoulder. (Fig 4-3-52)

Fig 4-3-49

Fig 4-3-50

Fig 4-3-51

Fig 4-3-52

4) Following partner B's leaning movement, partner A first rotates left forearm outward to ward off the oncoming force and turns torso slightly to the left to neutralize partner B's leaning force; next he draws in chest, turns waist to the left, shifts weight onto right leg, as hands change from deflecting to pressing movement—with left hand pressing partner B's left hand downward while right hand pressing partner B's left elbow; then he takes a quick step forward with left foot to place it by the inside of partner B's right foot. (Fig 4-3-53)

5) Following partner A's pressing movement, partner B uses the back of left hand to take on partner A's left hand, disengages right arm to rest it across partner A's left elbow; at the same time he moves right foot backward to the side of left foot, turning torso slightly to the left and changing from leaning to deflecting posture. Partner A still keeps left foot in front, bending left leg slightly and shifting weight a little forward. (Fig 4-3-54)

6) Partner B turns body to the left by moving left foot a step backward to the left, with both hands continuing the deflecting movement—left hand holding partner A's left wrist loosely and right wrist resting on his left elbow. Following partner B's deflecting movement, partner A takes a big step forward with right foot, shifting weight slightly forward onto right leg. (Fig 4-3-55)

7) Partner A moves left foot another step forward and places it by the inside of partner B's right foot, shift weight slightly forward onto left leg and at the same time rests right hand on the inside of left arm and leans towards partner B's chest with the force of left shoulder. (Fig 4-3-56)

In the above movements, the two partners are regarded to have completed a "cycle" when each has moved forward and backward once. To repeat the cycle, partner B moves right foot forward and starts pressing, while partner A retreats once again and changes to deflecting. The cycle can be repeated several times. (Figs 4-3-57, 4-3-58)

When partner B closes up, partner A moves left forearm downward to neutralize the leaning force and at the same time quickly strikes out at his face with right palm. Partner B raises right arm to take on partner A's right hand and grasps his wrist lightly, while his left resting wrist on partner A's right elbow. At the same time he turns body to the right, drawing back right foot to the side of left foot and starting a deflecting movement with both hands. Partner A receives partner B's deflecting force and shifts

Fig 4-3-53   Fig 4-3-54   Fig 4-3-55

Fig 4-3-56   Fig 4-3-57   Fig 4-3-58

weight slightly forward, moving right foot towards partner B's feet. (Figs 4-3-59, 4-3-60, 4-3--61)

8) Partner B turns body to the right and takes a sidestep with right foot, while both hands continue the deflecting movement. Led along by partner B's deflecting force, partner A takes a big step forward with left foot, shifting weight slightly forward; then he takes another step forward with right foot, placing it between partner B's feet. At the same time he rests left hand inside right arm and pushes both arms at partner B's chest. (Figs 4-3-61, 4-3-62)

The footwork in Figs 4-3-59, 4-3-62 is basically the same as that in Figs 49-56. The only difference is that in the latter case, partner A deflects partner B's right arm and partner B deflects partner A's left arm, and the method for a changeover lies in taking a quick step forward to turn deflecting to elbowing and then to pressing so as to neutralize the opponent's leaning force. In the former case, the aim of deflecting is to bend the opponent's right arm, and the key for a changeover lies in hitting at face with right palm.

In case partner A closes up on partner B, the latter may hit at the former's face with left palm. Then partner A uses left hand to hold partner B's left wrist loosely and turns body to the left, changing to a deflecting posture. Partner B moves right foot forward and closes up on partner A's chest with left arm. Following this, each side will hit at the other's face with left palm and have their left arms deflected. (Figs 4-3-63, 4-3-64, 4-3-65, 4-3-66)

Fig 4-3-59

Fig 4-3-60

Fig 4-3-61

Fig 4-3-62

Fig 4-3-63

Fig 4-3-64

Fig 4-3-65

Fig 4-3-66

Chapter Five
Qigong Health Care

1 Relaxation Qigong

Relaxation Qigong is a kind of Qigong exercise based on relaxation and stillness, including Patting-and-striking Relaxation, Partial Relaxation and Three-line Relaxation.

1.Patting-and-striking relaxation

The doctor pats the patient or the patient pats himself downward from the head to the feet. The sequence goes from the head (relax) → neck (relax) → shoulders (relax) → arms (relax) → hands (relax) → back and waist (relax) → chest and abdomen (relax) → thighs (relax) → shanks (relax) → feet (relax). Utter the word "relax" while patting and relax wherever the patting goes.

2. Partial relaxation

Take the body as several sections and relax them one by one in a downward direction under the guidance of mind intension, transversely from the head to the feet. The usual sequence is from the head (relax) → neck (relax) → shoulders (relax) → arms (relax) → hands (relax) → chest and back (relax) → waist and abdomen (relax) → thighs (relax) → shanks (relax) → feet (relax). The mind is focused on the section to be relaxed. Then silently read the word "relax" 2-3 times before shifting the mind-intension to the next section. Repeat the above procedure 3 times.

3. Three-line relaxation

The three lines refer to the following imaginary lines that begin at the head and end at the feet, running downwards respectively along the two sides, the front, and the back of the body. Keep mind concentration on the part of the body to be relaxed, saying stillness silently while inhaling and saying relaxation silently while exhaling.

The First Line (The Side Line)

Relax downwards from both sides of the head (relax) → both sides of the neck (relax) → shoulders (relax) → upper arms (relax) → elbow joints (relax) → forearms (relax) → wrist joints (relax) → palms (relax) → ten fingers of both hands (relax). Finally concentrate the mind on the tips of middle fingers for 1-2 minutes.

The Second Line (The Front Line)

Relax downwards along the front

line of the body from the face (relax) → neck (relax) → chest (relax) → abdomen (relax) → thighs (relax) → knees (relax) → shanks (relax) → insteps (relax) → ten toes of both feet (relax). Finally concentrate the mind on the big toes of both feet for 1-2 minutes.

The Third Line (The Back Line)

Relax downwards along the back line of the body from the occiput (relax) back side of the neck (relax) upper back (relax) lower back (relax) back sides of both thighs (relax) popliteal fossae (relax) back sides of both shanks (relax) heels (relax) soles (relax). Finally concentrate the mind on *yongquan* acupoint for 3-5 minutes.

Relax your body following the above three lines 3 times.

If a certain region or part of the body still has muscular tension, relax downwards once again so as to fulfill the purpose of whole body relaxation.

No matter which relaxation method you use, concentrate your mind on the abdominal *dantian* in the end and breathe naturally for 3-5 minutes.

4. Points for attention

(1) Posture

Any of the walking, sitting, standing and lying postures can be adopted, among which the regular sitting posture, the supine lying and natural standing are most frequently assumed.

(2) Breathing Method

Usually, the exercise of breathing is not stressed in Relaxation Qigong. You could just breathe naturally and transit natural breathing to abdominal respiration gradually. Say "stillness" silently while inhaling, and say "relaxation" silently while exhaling. In this way, you may enter the realm of relaxation and achieve stillness.

(3) Mind-intention

The mind-intention follows a downward sequence when doing Relaxation Qigong, i.e. from the head to the feet, and finally reaches the *yongquan* acupoint on the sole for the purpose of guiding *qi* to move downward from the head. In the closing form, guide *qi* to the abdominal *dantian*, concentrate mind on it for a moment, and then finish the exercise.

(4) Indications

Relaxation Qigong is effective for all chronic diseases, especially primary hypertension, neurasthenia, etc. Patients with chronic diseases or beginners who learn Qigong exercise for the purpose of health care should start from relaxation. It is enough for patients with syndrome of internal down-going *qi* to know the basic relaxation methods, since they are not able to practice for too long of a time. Instead, Health-Preservation Qigong or Standing Exercise is better for them in the long term. Partial relaxation should be adopted for shaking off the weariness after sports, supported by the three-line relaxation method.

(5) Duration of the exercise

The exercise should be practiced for 15-30 minutes for beginners and can be prolonged gradually after much practice.

II Ba-Duan-Jin (Eight Section Health Exercise)

Ba-Duan-Jin is a popular and widespread method for disease prevention and longevity, containing both a standing and sitting set of eight postures each.

Sitting Postures

1. Refreshing the spirit by closing the eyes

Use the cross-legged sitting posture with hands held gently in front of the lower abdomen. Center mind in *dantian* and adjust yourself gradually to abdominal breathing. Relax the body and spirit naturally for 3-5 minutes. (Fig 5-2-1)

2. Tapping the teeth

Tap the teeth 36 times and slowly swallow the saliva produced. Then cross fingers and hold hands up slowly. Passing the calvaria, place your hands on the occipital. Press forward with both palms clinging tightly to the occipital and the occipital pushed backward with force. Relax, press, relax and press for approximately a dozen times. Coordinating the actions with breathing, inhale while pressing and exhale while relaxing. (Fig 5-2-2)

3. Beating the heavenly drum

Place palms over ears with index fingers facing each other and clinging to the *yuzhen* acupoints on the sides of the head. Make middle fingers and index fingers crossed with index fingers on top. Then slide them down suddenly and forcefully to tap the *yuzhen* acupoints, producing a sound in the ears which resembles the beating of a drum. Tap 24 times simultaneously on the left and right sides and thereupon release both palms from ears. (Fig 5-2-3)

4. Shaking the head, resonant gargling, swallowing the saliva

Lift hands upward and put them down in front of chest and rest them at the root of thighs. Cross your fingers with palms facing upward. With head muscles in tension, shake your head leftward and rightward 24 times respectively. (Fig 5-2-4)

Then move the tongue as if gargling 36 times, making a gargling sound in the mouth. As the saliva increases, swallow it in three gulps. Guide it down by mind-intension into lower *dantian* and center mind there for a moment.

5. Rubbing the palms and the back

Sit up straight and breathe deeply with nose. Settle *qi* in the abdominal *dantian* with breath holding for a moment. Avoid suffocation. As soon as there is warm feeling in the abdomen, rub hands warm and massage *shenyu* acupoints on the sides of waist for about 20 times in a fast rhythm. Use mind-intention to guide *qi*, for the two going together will help to increase the warmth of the abdomen. Then exhale slowly with your nose. If you feel excessively warm, relax the mind-intension or adjust breathing to cool it down.(Fig 5-2-5)

6. Revolving the hands

Sit with legs stretching straight. Lift both hands from waist to chest with fingers naturally apart and slightly bent. Revolve the hands for 36 times and then reverse the movement. Keep your legs straight. As hands revolve, the upper body moves forward and backward in a narrow range. (Fig 5-2-6)

Fig 5-2-1

Fig 5-2-2

Fig 5-2-3

Fig 5-2-4

Fig 5-2-5

Fig 5-2-6

7. Holding up hands and pulling toes

Fingers interlocked, turn over palms with the center facing downward. Move in an upward arch until the hands reach above the crown of the head. With palms facing upward, exert your strength to push the hands up for 3 or 9 times and hold the posture for a moment. Then separate hands, bend forward and grasp the toes while keeping knees straight. Repeat the movement 11 times and then cross your legs and sit straight. (Fig 5-2-7)

8. Swallowing the saliva again

Close eyes and sit up straight, waiting the saliva to come (or move your tongue around inside your mouth to produce saliva). Gargle resonantly and swallow the saliva in three gulps. Repeat it 3 times. Then shrug your shoulders 20 times and swing your hands forward and backward for 24 times. Finally center mind in *dantian* adopting abdominal breathing. (Fig 5-2-8)

Fig 5-2-7

Fig 5-2-8

Standing Postures

1. Both hands holding up the sky

Starting Position

Stand naturally with feet shoulder-width apart and the hands hanging on sides naturally.

(1) Pose your hands as if you are holding something, palms facing upward, fingers of each hand pointing to each other. Slowly raise your hands from abdomen to chest height. Turn over hands with palms facing downward. Then forearms rotate inward and bring hands above the crown of head. Fully stretch up arms as if holding up the heavens. Simultaneously rise up on the toes and inhale. (Fig 5-2-9)

(2) Arms rotate outward, making palms facing each other. Lower both arms down in front of the body to both sides. Simultaneously return your feet to a flat footed position and exhale. Repeat the procedure 6 times.

2. Drawing the bow from both sides

(1) Step out with left foot into a horse-ride stance. Cross forearms at chest level, left in front of right. Extend left arm out to the left with forefinger pointing forward, thumb stretched back, and other fingers

slightly bent. Turn head to the left and look at left fingers. At the same time right arm moves out to the right keeping elbow bent and right hand clenched as if drawing a bow. (Fig 5-2-10)

(2) Open both fists and put down hands sideways, withdrawing the left foot to return to the starting position.

(3) Step out with right foot into a horse stance. Repeat movements in (1), reversing "right" and "left."

(4) Repeat movements in (2), reversing "right" and "left."

Repeat the procedure 6 times. Coordinate your movement with breathing. Inhale when drawing the arms up and exhale when returning to the starting position.

Fig 5-2-9

Fig 5-2-10

3. Raising one arm to regulate the spleen and stomach

(1) Raise your hands to chest height. Draw left hand up overhead with palm facing upward as holding up the sky, fingertips pointing to the right. At the same time, press right hand downward to the side of right hip with palm facing down and fingertips pointing forward. (Fig 5-2-11)

(2) Rotate left arm outward and down in front of the body with palm facing back. At the same time, move right arm upward in front of body so that both arms cross in front of chest

Fig 5-2-11

with right arm inside. Raise right hand overhead with palm facing upward like holding up the heavens and fingertips pointing to the left. Left hand is simultaneously pressed downward to the side of left hip with palm facing down and fingertips pointing forward.

Repeat the whole procedure 6 times. Inhale while lifting the arm and exhale while lowering the arm. Exhale when both hands are in front of chest and inhale when the arms are apart. Cross both hands in front of chest and lower them down sideways simultaneously to finish the form and assume the starting position.

4. Wise owl gazing backwards or looking back

(1) Inhale while slowly turning head to the right side as far as possible and look back as much as possible. (Fig 5-2-12)

(2) Then exhale and turn to the original position.

(3) Repeat movements in (1), reversing "right" and "left."

(4) Repeat movements in (2), reversing "right" and "left."

Repeat the whole procedure 6 times.

5. Swaying the head and swinging the buttocks

(1) Assume a horse stance and place palms on thighs with thumbs pointing backward. Look down and lean the upper trunk forward. Inhale while swaying the head to the left and swinging the buttocks to the right, aiding the movement by stretching left leg and arm. (Fig 5-2-13)

(2) Exhale while returning to the starting position.

(3) Repeat movements in (1), reversing "right" and "left."

(4) Repeat movements in (2).

Repeat the whole procedure 6 times.

6. Both hands holding the feet

(1) Stand straight. Bend over slowly and touch toes with hands (touch ankles or knees if toes can not be reached), keeping legs straight; keep head up slightly. Inhale at the start of the bend. (Fig 5-2-14)

(2) Exhale while returning to the starting position.

(3) Inhale while placing hands on the lower back, bending backward and stretching as far as you can.

(4) Exhale while returning to the starting position.

Repeat the whole procedure 6 times. You might find it difficult to coordinate the movement with respiration. Therefore, start practicing with natural breathing and gradually transmit to the coordinated breathing as required.

7. Clenching fists and glaring fiercely (or angrily)

(1) Take a horse stance with hands tightly clenched with palms facing upward at waist level. Punch slowly with right fist while rotating right arm until palm faces downward. Glare straight ahead and exhale. (Fig 5-2-15)

(2) Inhale while withdrawing the right fist beside the waist. Glare

Fig 5-2-12

Fig 5-2-13

Fig 5-2-14

Fig 5-2-15

straight ahead.

(3) Repeat movements in (1), reversing "right" and "left."

(4) Repeat movements in (2), reversing "right" and "left."

Repeat the whole procedure 6 times and then return to the starting position.

8. Bouncing on the Toes

(1) Inhale while raising the heels and stretching up on the toes. Try to apply maximum strength to the upward push. (Fig 5-2-16)

(2) Exhale while lowering the heels and returning to the starting position.

Repeat the whole procedure 6 times.

Efficacy of Ba-Duan-Jin and Points for Attention

It's convenient to practice Ba-Duan-Jin, be it in the fresh air in the early morning or in bed before going to sleep. The times and contents of practice are also flexible varying with specific circumstances. Exhale with nose while practicing the sitting postures. Continuous practice (3 times every day) would promote the smooth circulation of blood and balance *yin* and *yang*. To achieve a better result, it can be combined with 20 minutes' static exercises under the guidance of minor-celestial-circle circulation method. The standing postures play an effective

Fig 5-2-16

role in regulating the spleen and stomach as well as the triple energizer, expelling the heart-fire, and reinforcing the loins and kidneys so as to build up strength in an all-round way.

Beginners should first learn the postures well and then coordinate them with breathing and mind-intention. Only by the combination of the three could the efficacy of the exercise be promoted. The principle of "relaxing the body and spirit naturally" should be followed throughout the practice. Motion and stillness combing together would help to develop both spiritually and physically. Besides, practitioners should remember to center the mind in *dantian* for a moment and breathe naturally ten times before ending the exercises.

III Five-Animal Play (Wu-Qin-Xi)

As a kind of therapeutical exercise based on the theories of traditional Chinese medicine, Five-Animal Play must be performed with a tranquillized mind, relaxed body and mobilized muscles and joints. Breathing must be deep, soft and even. The will leads the *qi* to circulate through the body.

Hua Tuo's original set of Five-Animal Play is long extinct, but many different schools have appeared over the centuries. The following set was recently compiled by Zhou Nian-Feng, associate professor at Tianjin Institute of Traditional Chinese Medicine, with extensive reference to historical documents and existing routines. With its simple movements, it is easy for beginners to learn. The amount of exercise for each section may vary from person to person according to his health condition. Persistent regular practice has proved wholesome for improving one's health.

Bear Play

Opening posture: Stand upright with feet shoulder-width apart, arms hanging naturally. Take 3-5 deep breaths. (Fig 5-3-1)

1) Bend right knee with right shoulder protruding forward and downward, right arm dropped. At the same time, protrude left shoulder backward and outward, left arm raised a little. (Fig 5-3-2)

2) Bend left knee with left shoulder protruding forward and downward, left arm dropped. At the same time, protrude right shoulder backward and outward with right arm raised a little.

Fig 5-3-1

Fig 5-3-2

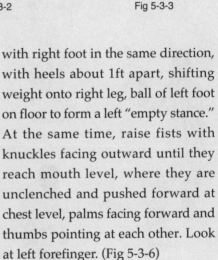

Fig 5-3-3

(Fig 5-3-3)

Repeat these movements.

Tiger Play

Opening posture: Stand upright with feet together, arms hanging naturally, neck held erect, eyes looking ahead, mouth closed and tip of tongue lightly touching hard palate. Keep whole body relaxed without protruding chest or hunching back. (Fig 5-3-4)

1. Left style

1) Bend both knees slowly, shifting body weight onto right leg and raising left heel close to right ankle, ball of left foot on floor. At the same time, clench both hands and raise them to waist height, palms up and look forward to the left. (Fig 5-3-5)

2) Take a step forward with left foot to the left front and then half a step with right foot in the same direction, with heels about 1ft apart, shifting weight onto right leg, ball of left foot on floor to form a left "empty stance." At the same time, raise fists with knuckles facing outward until they reach mouth level, where they are unclenched and pushed forward at chest level, palms facing forward and thumbs pointing at each other. Look at left forefinger. (Fig 5-3-6)

2. Right style

1) Bring right foot to left foot, with right heel off floor and both knees bent a little. At the same time, clench both hands and withdraw them to waist height, fists palms-up. Look forward to the right. (Fig 5-3-7)

2) Repeat movements in 2) for left style, reversing "right" and "left." (Fig 5-3-8) Alternate left and right in exercise.

Fig 5-3-4

Fig 5-3-5

Fig 5-3-6

Fig 5-3-7

Fig 5-3-8

Ape Play

Opening posture: Same as that for Tiger Play.

1) Bend both knees slowly and take a light step forward with left foot. At the same time, raise left hand to mouth level where it moves forward as if to grasp something and turns into a claw at last, wrist curved naturally downward. (Fig 5-3-9)

2) Take a step forward with right foot and half a step with left foot, heel off floor. At the same time, raise right hand to mouth level where it moves forward as if to feel for something and turns into a claw when it is near end-position, wrist curved naturally down-ward, while left hand with-draws to waist-side. (Fig 5-3-10)

3) Take a short step backward with left foot, heel on floor, and sit back, moving body backward as if to take a seat; move right foot a bit backward, toes touching the floor. At the same time, raise left hand to mouth level where it moves forward as if to grasp something and turns into a claw at last, wrist curved naturally downward, while right hand withdraws to waist-side. (Fig 5-3-11)

4) Repeat movements in 3), reversing "right" and "left." (Fig 5-3-12)

5) Repeat movements in 2), reversing "right" and "left." (Fig 5-3-13)

6) Repeat movements in 3), revers-

ing "right" and "left." (See Fig 5-3-11)

These may go on as many times as you choose.

Deer Play

Opening posture: Same as that for Tiger Play.

1) Bend right knee and sit back, stretching left leg forward with knee bent a little and ball of left foot on floor to form a left empty stance. At the same time, stretch left hand forward with elbow bent a little and place right hand inside left elbow, both palms facing inward. (Fig 5-3-14)

2) Circle both arms counterclockwise in front of chest, left arm in larger circles. At the same time, circle hips in unison with the arm movement, as if arms were set in motion by hips, in the manner of "a deer moving with its tail-root as the hinge."

3) Take a step forward with right foot to form a right empty stance and place left hand inside right elbow. Circle arms and hips clockwise.

Repeat these movements.

Bird Play

Opening posture: Same as that for Tiger Play.

1) Take a step forward with left foot and half a step with right foot, toes on floor. At the same time, raise hands in front of chest and stretch arms side-

Fig 5-3-9

Fig 5-3-10

Fig 5-3-11

Fig 5-3-12

Fig 5-3-13

Fig 5-3-14

Fig 5-3-15   Fig 5-3-16   Fig 5-3-17

ways over-head, inhaling deeply. (Fig 5-3-15)

2) Bring right foot to left foot and drop yourself into a full squat, lowering both arms to cross them in front of shins with the palm facing up. Exhale deeply at the same time. (Fig 5-3-16)

3) Repeat movements in 1), reversing "right" and "left." (Fig 5-3-17)

4) Repeat movements in 2), reversing "right" and "left."(Fig 5-3-16)

This may go on for as many times as you choose.

Chapter Six
Self-Massage

Self-massage is an important part of Chinese traditional health care exercises, boasting a long history. It has been developed over the past thousands of years by many *kungfu* practitioners and physicians through their practical experience, along with other accessible and efficient health care exercises. Based on the specific connection between *zangfu* organs, meridians and collaterals, as well as the important role of acupoints in human body, this exercise helps to relax the muscles, activate the *qi* and blood circulation, accelerate the metabolism and enhance the physiological function by combining local massage with whole-body massage along meridians, which in turn contributes to health improvement and disease prevention and treatment.

1 Sixteen Tips for Health Care Massage

1. Combing your hair

Combing your hair and scalp frequently can open up the circulation of *qi* and blood in the head and activate central nervous system, hence helping to gain a sober and healthy brain. Meanwhile, dizziness, swelling feel in the head and headache can be prevented and cured.

2. Rolling your eyes

Eyes (including the rim of eye socket) should be pressed, rubbed and revolved regularly, which will enhance eyesight, prevent and cure eye diseases.

3. Scrubbing your face

Constantly pressing, rubbing, kneading and scrubbing your face, from forehead to chin, including both temples and sides of your nose bridge can get you away from common cold, headache, dizziness, swelling feel in the head, toothache, stuffy nose and aging.

4. Flicking your ears

If you knead, scrub, shake and flick your ears regularly, or in the commonly heard expression on "beating the heavenly drum and scrubbing the helix," your hearing can be sharpened and ear diseases prevented and cured.

5. Pressing the tip of your tongue against the palate

Putting the tip of your tongue against your palate can make more saliva, which helps digestion and

7. Swallowing the saliva

Don't spit saliva; instead we should swallow it and use it to digest foods and build up appetite.

8. Expiring the waste air

The waste air in your body should be expired out. Keep doing this and breathing in the fresh air through expiration and inspiration exercise will help cure diseases and built up health.

9. Warming your back

Moving, pressing and rubbing your back regularly to keep it warm will help circulation of *qi* and blood in your back and thus cure and prevent backache and lumbago.

Old people practicing Taijijian on the square in Shenyang, Liaoning Province, 1986.

concentration for peaceful mental status.

6. Tapping your teeth

Tap your teeth frequently, first the lateral teeth, then the front teeth. By doing so over time, more saliva will be secreted, teeth will get firmer and healthier, and dental diseases will be prevented and cured.

10. Protecting your chest

Most essential visceral organs, for instance the heart, are located inside your chest, so we should take positive measures such as expiration and inspiration exercise and massage to prevent lung and heart problems.

11. Rubbing your abdomen

Abdomen here refers to gastric cavity and the lower abdomen below navel. A constant massage of this part will promote activity of stomach and intestines, which in turn contributes to the prevention and treatment of epigastric pain, abdominal distension, abdominal pain, indigestion, constipation, neurasthenia, insomnia, etc.

12. Lifting and contracting gudao

Gudao is another name for the anus. The frequent conscious contraction of it can help consolidate and reinforce the vital essence, cure deficiency syndromes and diseases due to collapse of *qi* of the middle energizer, for instance, spermatorrhea, enuresis, loose stool, hemorrhoids and prolapse of uterus, etc.

13. Rotating your limbs

The joints of the limbs should be turned frequently, which can prevent and cure arthritis of the elbow, wrist, knee and ankle.

14. Scrubbing your sole

Constantly pressing and rubbing

At the launching ceremony of the first Fitness Day in Beijing on Aug. 8, 2009, 33,996 people were practicing Taijiquan, which broke the Guiness world records.

yongquan acupoint on your sole serves as a good cure for hypertension, dizziness, neurasthenia and insomnia, etc. Better effects can be achieved if the abdomen is simultaneously pressed and rubbed.

15. Keeping your skin dry

Keep your skin dry for most of the time. Scrubbing the water off your skin and rubbing skin till it turns red after bathing and washing your hands and feet will prevent and cure diseases caused by the invasion of humidity into your body, like common cold and rheumatism.

16. Don't speak while relieving yourself

Keeping silent with your jaw locked when you are relieving yourself has the efficacy of reinforcing kidney, strengthening teeth, preventing and curing tooth diseases.

II Commonly Adopted Self-Massage

1. Patting the skullcap and rubbing *baihui* acupoint

As the headquarters of the body, calvaria (skullcap) are the source of all *yang* meridians and the cradle of the entire cerebrocentric nervous system. *Baihui* acupoint sitting at the center of the head-top is the meeting point of all collaterals. Being a crucial point of keeping physically strong and spiritually calm, it is effective in refreshing the mind, expelling pathogenic cold, removing excessive *yang* from the liver, and lifting the sinking of *yang-qi* and plays a supplementary role in treating various deficiency and excess syndromes.

2. Scrubbing the bridge of nose and pressing *taiyang* acupoint

Knead and scrub both sides of the bridge of the nose; knead and press *yintang, taiyang, renzhong, fengchi* acupoints, etc. This method can be used for the prevention and treatment for diseases and syndromes like common cold, headache, dizziness, toothache and epistaxis (nosebleed).

3. Pressing *fengchi* acupoint and scrubbing the coccyx and rumpbone

Fengchi acupoint sitting in the depression of the lateral sides of the two great muscles and tendons on the back of the neck is an important acupoint in the gallbladder meridian. Pressing *fengchi* acupoint with both thumbs and scrubbing the coccyx and rumpbone with both palms are effective in curing such diseases as neurasthenia, insomnia, hypertension, headache, dizziness, etc.

4. Grasping the mid-shoulder acupoint and pinching the nape

The mid-shoulder refers to *jianjing* acupoint while the nape to the portion between back hair line and *dazhui* acupoint, including *Du* meridian and the great muscles and tendons on its lateral sides. This method can help regulate *yang-qi* in the whole body, prevent and cure diseases like pain in shoulder, back or nape, stiff neck, fever, etc.

5. Rubbing the chest and pressing the back

Rubbing the chest means pressing and rubbing the portion around the pit of the stomach. "Back" here refers to the spinal column (of *Du* meridian) and the region on its sides, 6th -11th vertebra and its lateral acupoints in particular. Rubbing the chest can cure chest distress, costalgia, palpitation, shortness of breath, etc. while pressing the back acupoints can function as the treatment to diseases like pain in

the upper abdomen.

6. Pressing *feishu* and *gaohuang* acupoints and pinching the front side of the neck

The front side of the neck refers to the throat and the muscle and tendon on its sides. Kneading, pressing, pinching and grasping both the acupoints can help cure diseases like common cold, cough, asthma, pain in the throat, vomiting, as well as various deficiency syndromes.

7. Pinching the gastric cavity and squeezing the region surrounding the navel

The gastric cavity mainly refers to *zhongwan* acupoint and its surrounding region, including *Ren*, stomach and kidney meridians. Pinching and squeezing this part serves as the cure for pain in the gastric cavity and the upper abdomen, vomiting, diarrhea, constipation, etc.

8. Rubbing *dantian* and pinching mamipura chakra

Rubbing *dantian* (the abdomen region below navel) has favorable effects in treating indigestion, abdominal distension, diarrhea, constipation, spermatorrhea, impotence, prospermia, dysmenorrhea, metror-

Students from the No.3 Experimental Primary School in Linyi, Shandong province are practicing neck self-massage.

rhagia and metrostaxis, morbid leukorrhagia, hypertension, neurasthenia, insomnia, etc. After rubbing *dantian*, pinch the mamipura chakra for several minutes to end the procedure.

9. Pressing *yaoyan* and scrubbing *shenshu* acupoint

Yaoyan is in the depression in the lower part of the back on both sides of the lumbar vertebra. *Shenshu* acupoint also sits in this region. Regularly kneading and pressing *yaoyan* and scrubbing *shenshu* acupoint (including the *mingmen* acupoint between the kidneys) can help prevent and cure lumbago and back soreness and pain, strengthen waist and nourish kidneys, and has good effect on diseases like irregular menstruation, morbid leukorrhagia, spermatorrhea, etc.

10. Heavily-pressing *zusanli* and point-knocking *hegu*

Zusanli and *hegu* are important acupoints of Foot-Yangming and Hand-Yangming meridians. Pressing, kneading and rubbing these two acupoints with different forces can cure cold (including flu), headache, toothache, tonsillitis, as well as diseases of the stomach and intestines.

11. Scrubbing, kneading and revolving elbows and knees

Elbows here refer to the posterior protrusion at the elbow joint while knees to the anterior protrusion to the knee joint. Kneading, scrubbing and revolving elbows and knees can strengthen the arms, prevent and cure inflammation of the arms and olenitis. Applying this method to the knees can strengthen the legs, prevent and cure gonarthritis.

12. Pinching the depressions anterior to the elbow joint and grasping the popliteal fossae

The three *yin* meridians of hand runs through the anterior depressions to the elbow joints while Foot-taiyang meridian runs through the popliteal fossa. Pinching and grasping the former can help treat upper limbs soreness and pain, scapulodynia, laryngalgia, heatstroke, vomiting, etc. Pinching and grasping the latter is effective to lower limbs soreness and pain, abdominal pain, diarrhea, laryngalgia, heatstroke, lumbago, etc. In addition, patting and pressing the forearms and calves can make the flow of *qi* and blood go downward, which is effective to the prevention and cure of hypertension.

13. Kneading the lateral malleolus and nipping the heels

Three *yin* meridians of foot and *yang* meridians of hand run through the surrounding region of the medial and lateral malleolus while Foot-taiyang and kidney meridians pass the heels. Clinical experience proves that pressing, kneading, rubbing, pinching and squeezing the lateral malleolus (and its surrounding acupoints) has the function of calming down all nerves, helping regain keen consciousness and induce resuscitation. As a cure for various pain and inflammation syndromes, it is especially effective to headache, toothache, abdominal pain and lumbago.

14. Rubbing *laogong* and scrubbing *yongquan* points

Sitting on the palm, *laogong*, a crucial acupoint of heart meridian, plays the role of clearing away heart-fire, removing heat from the blood, removing dampness, easing the mind and regulating the stomach. The acupoint is also a key point for refining, accumulating, circulating and exiting the outer *qi*. *Yongquan*, whose function has been given specially regarded to by *kungfu* practitioners of past ages, is an acupoint of the kidney meridian on the sole, with the function of clearing away the heat and fire and helping to regain keen consciousness and calm down. Rubbing *yongquan* acupoint on the sole and *laogong* acupoint on the palm can give play to the dual function of both acupoints, which has favorable supplementary effect in treating diseases like hypertention, neurasthenia, insomnia, dizziness, spermatorrhea, etc. Continuous and perseverant practice will contribute to the coordination between the heart and the kidney

Each time practitioners can select a few from the above-mentioned four-

teen self-massage methods in accordance to their physical condition. A top-down sequence should be followed in the course of practice no matter how many methods are selected. In addition, mind-intension should be concentrated on the region or acupoint that is point-knocked, pressed with difference forces, or rubbed, so as to achieve the state of "convergence of intension, *qi* and strength at the point." This convergence will greatly enhance the efficacy.

III Local and Meridian-Corresponding Self-Massage

Local and meridian-corresponding self-massage is compiled in accordance to the specific connection between head, face, chest, abdomen, limbs and *zangfu* organs, meridians and collaterals, as well as *yin*, *yang*, *qi*, blood, that go along all their channels according to TCM. With the main function of opening meridians and collaterals, regulating *ying* and *wei*, the flow of *qi* and blood, it contributes to disease prevention and treatment and health promotion. To enhance the efficacy, it is recommended to be practiced after the static exercises. As all *yang* meridians meet in head and face, all *yin* meridians meet in chest and

abdomen, and all the twelve meridians linking with *zangfu* organs meet, exit, enter and circulate in four limbs, to combine local massage of head, face, chest and abdomen with the massage along the meridians of the limbs would achieve better therapeutic results.

Local meridian-corresponding self-massage consists of five exercises, which can be practiced under the following instructions.

1. Massaging the head and the face (five sections, 7 times each section)

(1) Resonant gargling, swallowing

the saliva and tapping the teeth

Gargle to produce the saliva and swallow it in 3 gulps; tap the teeth, first lateral teeth and then front teeth.

(2) Rolling and scrubbing the eyes

Open eyes wide gazing far into distance and then turn to the tip of the nose. Do it alternately. Then scrub the upper side of eye socket along the eye brow first and then the lower side of it.

(3) Scrubbing and rubbing the face and forehead

Place your palms beside the bridge of the nose and scrub it up and down. Then rub your forehead with palms leftward and rightward.

(4) Rubbing the vertex and scrubbing the nape

Rub from the forehead to the skull top with palms and then from the skull top to both sides of the nape.

(5) Beating the "heavenly drum" and rubbing the ear helix

Cover both ears with palms. Place index fingers on middle fingers and then slip the former continuously to produce a drum-beating sound. Thereupon rub ears with palms up and down from ear-tip to ear-root.

2. Massaging the chest and the abdomen

(1) Scrubbing the chest

Pressing and scrubbing the chest downward and rightward. Then mas-

sage in circling rout the *jiuwei* acupoint below the breastbone.

(2) Scrubbing the abdomen

Scrub the *dantian* first. Then use left hand to conduct a left-to-right massage circling the navel in the length between *zhongwan* and *zhongji* acupoints. Convert to a right-to-left massage with right hand. Then, reverse direction. Thereupon rub the abdomen upward from pubis to navel.

3. Massaging the limbs (upper limbs to lower limbs, left to right and outside to inside)

(1) Massaging the upper limbs

Massage along three *yang* meridians of hand from the lateral side of the palm to the shoulder and then following three *yin* meridians of hand from the shoulder along the inner side of the arm to the hand. Reverse the hands and repeat the movement.

(2) Massaging the lower limbs

Massage along three *yang* meridians of foot from lateral thigh to the feet and then following three *yin* meridians of foot from medial side of the ankle up to groin. Coordinate the movement with breathing.

(3) Shaking the hands and kicking with heel

Shake the wrist up and down, left and right for 7 times respectively. Then lift the tiptoe, kick with heel forcefully and pull back. Repeat the movement 7 times.

(4) Scrubbing *laogong* and rubbing *yongquan* acupoints

After palms are scrubbed warm, rub *yongquan* on the sole with *laogong* acupoint on the palm.

4. Knocking *dantian* and tapping *mingmen* acupoint

Clench both hands and knock *dantian* with one hand while tapping *mingmen* acupoint with the other alternately. Turn your waist to coordinate with the movement.

5. Closing form

(1) Center mind in *dantian* and guide inner *qi* to gather towards it from all around with both hands.

(2) Take a long breath while lifting anus.

(3) Hold breath for a moment while holding *dantian* with both palms facing inward.

Any of the walking, sitting, standing and lying postures can be adopted while conducting self-massage, among which the sitting posture are more frequently assumed. However, it is advisable to apply standing posture to the practice of tapping *dantian* and knocking *mingmen* acupoints. In addition, self-massage may be performed in four seasons year round. But the method of patting and striking instead of pressing and scrubbing should be adopted when it is applied to the chest, abdomen and limbs due to the inconvenience of reaching the skin with more clothes on in winter. The intensity, times and rhythm depend on the state of illness and personal constitution.

Glossary 1: Terms of Exercises

Pin Yin	English	Chinese
An	Pushing	按
Ba-Duan-Jin	Eight-Section Health Exercise	八段锦
Bai He Liang Chi	White Crane Spreading Its Wings	白鹤亮翅
Cun	A unit of length equal to one-third decimeter	寸
Dan Bian	Single Whip	单鞭
Dao-Yin-Shu	Physical and Breathing Exercise	导引术
Dazhoutian	Major celestial circle	大周天
Donggong	Dynamic exercise	动功
Dongjinggong	Combined exercise	动静功
Fang-Song-Gong	Relaxation Qigong	放松功
Gao-Tan-Ma	Patting the Horse on the Back	高探马
Ji	Pressing	挤
Jinggong	Static exercise	静功
Hai-Di-Zhen	Thrusting the Hand Downward	海底针
Jing, Qi, Shen	Vital essence, qi and vitality	精气神
Jing-Zuo-Gong	Sit-still Exercise	静坐功
Jinli	Strength	劲力
Lü	Rolling Back	捋
Man-Bu-Xing-Gong	Slow-walking Exercise	慢步行功
Peng	Warding Off	掤
Ru Feng Si Bi	Apparent Sealing and Closing	如封似闭
Shan-Tong-Bi	Unfurling Arms like a Fan	闪通臂
Shi'er-Duan-Jin	Twelve-section Health Exercise	十二段锦
Shiliu-Duan-Jin	Sixteen-section Health Exercise	十六段锦
Shi-Zi-Shou	Crossing Hands	十字手
Shou Hui Pi Pa	Playing the Lute	手挥琵琶
Shuang Feng Guan Er	Striking Opponent's Ears with Both Fists	双峰贯耳
Song-Jing-Gong	Relaxation-tranquility Qigong	松静功

Pin Yin	English	Chinese
Taijijian	Taiji Swordplay	太极剑
Taijiquan	Taijiquan	太极拳
Tiaoshen	Regulating the body	调身
Tiaoxi	Regulating breath	调息
Tiaoxin	Regulating the mind	调心
Tuishou	Push hand	推手
Wu-Qin-Xi	Five-Animal-Play	五禽戏
Wu Shu	Wu Shu	武术
Xiaozhoutian	Minor celestial circle	小周天
Yi-Jin-Jing	Changing Tendons Exercise	易筋经
Yinian	Mind-intension	意念
You-Deng-Jiao	Kicking with Right Heel	右蹬脚
You Lan Que Wei	Grasping the Peacock's Tail-Right Style	右揽雀尾
You Xia Shi Du Li	Snake Creeping Down and Golden Rooster Standing on Right Leg	右下势独立
Yun Shou	Waving Hands Like Floating Clouds—Left Style	云手
Zhan-Zhuang-Gong	Standing Exercise	站桩功
Zhuan Shen Ban Lan Chui	Deflecting, Parrying and Punching	转身搬拦捶
Zhuan Shen Zuo Deng Jiao	Kicking with Left Heel	转身左蹬脚
Zuo Lan Que Wei	Grasping the Peacock's Tail—Left Style	左揽雀尾
Zuo Xia Shi Du Li	Snake Creeping Down and Golden Rooster Standing on Left Leg	左下势独立
Zuo You Chuan Suo	Working at Shuttles on Both Sides	左右穿梭
Zuo You Dao Juan Gong	Stepping Back and Whirling Arms on Both Sides	左右倒卷肱
Zuo You Lou Xi Ao Bu	Brushing Knees and Twisting Steps	左右搂膝拗步
Zuo You Ye Ma Fen Zong	Parting the Wild Horse's Mane	左右野马分鬃

Glossary 2: Terms of Meridians Collaterals Acupoints

Baihui	Hundred convergences	百会
Bieluo	Major collaterals	别络
Changqiang	Long strong	长强
Chengjiang	Saliva receiving	承浆
Chengshan	Mountain support	承山
Dazhui	Great hammer	大椎
Feishu	Lung shu	肺俞
Fengchi	Wind pond	风池
Fengfu	Wind mansion	风府
Fuluo	Superficial collaterals	浮络
Gaohuang	Vitals	膏肓
Gudao	Anus	谷道
Hegu	Union valley	合谷
Huiyin	Meeting of yin	会阴
Jiaji	Spine	夹脊
Jianjing	Shoulder well	肩井
Jingjin	Muscle meridians	经筋
Jing Luo	Meridians and collaterals	经络
Mingmen	Life gate	命门
Pibu	Skin areas	皮部
Qihai	Reservoir of Qi	气海
Qijing Bamai	Eight extraordinary meridians	奇经八脉
Quchi	Pool at the Bend	曲池
Queqiao	Magpie bridge	鹊桥
Renzhong	Middle-of-Man	人中
Sanguan	Three passes	三关
Shanzhong	Middle chest	膻中
Shenque	Navel	神阙
Shenshu	Kidney shu	肾俞
Shou-Jueyin Xinbaojing	Hand-Jueyin Pericardium Meridian	手厥阴心包经

Shou-Shaoyang Sanjiaojing	Hand-Shaoyang Triple Energizer Meridian	手少阳三焦经
Shou-Shaoyin Xinjing	Hand-Shaoyin Heart Meridian	手少阴心经
Shou-Taiyang Xiaochangjing	Hand-Taiyang Small Intestine Meridian	手太阳小肠经
Shou-Taiyin Feijing	Hand-Taiyin Lung Meridian	手太阴肺经
Shou-Yangming Dachangjing	Hand-Yangming Large Intestine Meridian	手阳明大肠经
Taiyang	Supreme yang	太阳
Tianting	Middle forehead	天庭
Tiantu	Sky prominence	天突
Weigu	Coccyx	尾骨
Weizhong	Bend middle	委中
Yaoyan	Lumber eyes	腰眼
Yintang	Glabella	印堂
Yongquan	Gushing spring	涌泉
Yuzhen	Jade Pillow	玉枕
Zhongwan	Middle epigastrium	中脘
Zhongji	Central pole	中极
Zu-Jueyin Ganjing	Foot-Jueyin Liver Meridian	足厥阴肝经
Zusanli	Leg three li	足三里
Zu-Shaoyang Danjing	Foot-Shaoyang Gallbladder Meridian	足少阳胆经
Zu-Shaoyin Shenjing	Foot-Shaoyin Kidney Meridian	足少阴肾经
Zu-Taiyang Pangguangjing	Foot-Taiyang Bladder Meridian	足太阳膀胱经
Zu-Taiyin Pijing	Foot-Taiyin Spleen Meridian	足太阴脾经
Zu-Yangming Weijing	Foot-Yangming Stomach Meridian	足阳明胃经

CHINESE PHYSICAL EXERCISES AND HEALTH CARE